Soccer:

A Step-by-Step Guide on How to Outsmart Your Opponents and Improve Your Mentality, How to Get a Good Night's Sleep Every Single Night, and How to Fuel a Great Performance

Dylan Joseph

Soccer:
A Step-by-Step Guide on How to Outsmart Your Opponents and
Improve Your Mentality, How to Get a Good Night's Sleep Every
Single Night, and How to Fuel a Great Performance
By: Dylan Joseph
© 2021
All Rights Reserved

WAIT!

Wouldn't it be nice to have an easy three-page checklist and summary guide of this book's steps? Well, here is your chance!

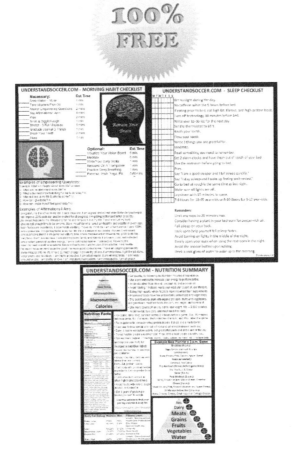

Go to this Link for an **Instant** Three-Page Printout:
UnderstandSoccer.com/free-printout

This FREE checklist and summary guide is simply a thank you for purchasing this book.

Soccer:
A Step-by-Step Guide on How to Outsmart Your Opponents and Improve Your Mentality, How to Get a Good Night's Sleep Every Single Night, and How to Fuel a Great Performance
All Rights Reserved
April 3, 2021
Copyright © 2021 Understand, LLC
Dylan@UnderstandSoccer.com
Printed in the United States of America

Table of Contents

Preface

Soccer Mindset dives deep into how having a mentally tough mindset can be the difference from average performances and lifting the trophy at the end of the season. Because all action originates in your mind, if you can train your mind to succeed, the actions and results you want will follow.

Soccer Sleep reveals how to become an amazing sleeper that understands how to set yourself up for sleeping success and how to overcome feeling "foggy" on those days where you did not obtain enough hours of sleep.

Soccer Nutrition discusses what things make the biggest difference for a soccer player, it will help you understand how to make eating healthy a habit that you do not even have to think about, and how to get an edge over your competition.

INDIVIDUAL SOCCER PLAYER'S PYRAMID

If you are looking to improve your skills, your child's confidence, or your players' abilities, it is essential to understand where this book fits into the bigger picture of developing a soccer player. In the image, you can see the most critical field-specific skills to work on are at the base of the Individual Soccer Player's Pyramid. The pyramid is a quality outline that you can use to improve an individual soccer player's game. All the elements in the pyramid and the items surrounding it play a meaningful part in becoming a better player, but certain skills should be read and mastered first before moving to the others.

You will notice that passing and receiving is at the foundation of the pyramid because if you can receive a pass and make a pass in soccer, you will be a useful teammate. Though you may not be the one that is consistently scoring, the person that is dispossessing the other team, or the player that can dribble through several opponents, you will have the fundamental tools needed to play the sport and contribute to your team.

As you move one layer up, you find yourself with a decision to make on how to progress. Specifically, the pyramid is created with you in mind because each soccer player and each soccer position have different needs. Therefore, your choice regarding which path to take first is dictated by the position you play and more importantly, by the position that you want to play. In soccer and life, just because you are in a particular spot, position, or even a job, it does not mean that you have to stay there forever if that is not your choice. However, it is not recommended to refuse playing a position if you are not in the exact role you want. It takes time to develop the skills that will allow you to make a shift from one position to another.

If you want to become a forward, then consider starting your route on the second layer of the pyramid with shooting and finishing. As your abilities to shoot increase, your coach will notice your new finishing skills and will be more likely to move you up the field if you are not a forward already. Be sure to communicate to the coach that you desire to be moved up the field to a more offensive position, which will increase your chances, as well. If you are already a forward, then dive deep into this topic to ensure you become the leading scorer; first on your team, and then in the entire league. Notice that shooting and finishing is considered less critical than passing and receiving because you have to pass the ball up the field before you can take a shot on net.

Otherwise, you can start by progressing to dribbling & foot skills from passing & receiving because the proper technique is crucial to dribble the ball well. It is often necessary for a soccer player to use a skill to protect the ball from the other team or to advance the ball up the field to place their team in a favorable situation to score. The selection of this route is often taken first by midfielders and occasionally by forwards.

Defending is another option of how you can proceed from passing and receiving. Being able to keep the other team off the scoreboard is not an easy task. Developing a defender's mindset, learning which way to push a forward, understanding how to position your body, knowing when to foul, and using the correct form for headers is critical to a defender on the back line looking to prevent goals.

Finish all three areas in the second layer of the pyramid before progressing up the pyramid. Dribbling and defending the ball (not just shooting) are useful for an attacker, shooting and defending (not just dribbling) are helpful for a midfielder, while shooting and dribbling (not just defending) are helpful for a defender. Having a well-rounded knowledge of the skills needed for the different positions is important for all soccer players. It is especially essential for those soccer players looking to change positions in the future. Shooting and finishing, dribbling and foot skills, and defending are oftentimes more beneficial for soccer players to learn first than the next tier of the pyramid, so focus on these before spending time on areas higher up in the pyramid. In addition, reading about each of these areas will help you to understand what your opponent wants to do as well.

Once you have improved your skills in the first and second tiers of the pyramid, move up to fitness. As you practice everything below this category on the pyramid, your fitness and strength will naturally increase. It is difficult to go through a passing/dribbling/finishing drill for a few minutes without being out of breath. Performing technical drills allows soccer players to increase their fitness naturally. This reduces the need to focus exclusively on running for fitness. Coming from a soccer player and trainer (i.e., someone with a view from both sides), I know that constantly focusing on running is not as fulfilling and does not create long-lasting improvements, whereas emphasizing shooting capabilities, foot skills, and defending knowledge creates long-lasting change. Often, coaches who focus on running their players in practice are also coaches who want to improve their team but have limited knowledge of many of the soccer-specific topics that would quickly increase their players' abilities. Not only does fitness in soccer include your endurance; it also addresses your ability to run with agility and speed, develop strength and power, while improving your flexibility through stretching to become a well-rounded soccer player.

Similar to the tier below it, you should focus on the fitness areas that will help you specifically, while keeping all of the topics in mind. For example, you may be a smaller soccer player who could use some size. In this case, you should emphasize weight training so that you can gain the muscle needed to avoid being pushed off the ball. However, you should still stretch before and after a lifting workout or soccer practice/game to ensure that you stay limber and flexible to recover quickly and avoid injuries.

Maybe you are a soccer player in your 20s, 30s, or 40s. Then, emphasizing your flexibility would do a world of good to ensure you keep playing soccer for many more years. However, doing a few sets of push-ups, pull-ups, squats, lunges, sit-ups, etc. per week will help you maintain or gain a desirable physique.

Furthermore, you could be in the prime of your career in high school, college, or at the pro level, which means that obtaining the speed and endurance needed to run for 90+ minutes is the most essential key to continue pursuing your soccer aspirations.

Finally, we travel to the top of the pyramid which involves tryouts. Though tryouts occur only one to two times per year, they have a huge impact on whether you make the team you want to join or get left out of the lineup. Tryouts can cause intense nerves if you do not know the keys to making sure that you stand out and are very confident from the start.

If you have not read the *Understand Soccer* series book, *Soccer Training*, it is highly recommended that you do to gain the general knowledge of crucial topics within the areas of the pyramid. Picking up a copy of the book will act as a good gauge to see how much you know about each topic, which will help determine if a book later in the series written about a specific subject in the soccer pyramid will be beneficial for you.

The last portion of the pyramid are the areas that surround the pyramid. Though these are not skills and topics that can be addressed by your physical abilities, they each play key roles in rounding out a complete soccer player. For example, having a supportive parent/guardian or two is beneficial for transporting the child to games, providing the equipment needed, the fees for the team, expenses for individual training, and encouragement. Having a quality coach whose teachings and drills help the individual learn how their performance and skills fit into the team's big picture helps a lot too.

Sleeping enough is critical to having energy in practices and on game days, in addition to recovering from training and games. Appropriate soccer nutrition will increase a soccer player's energy and endurance, help them achieve the ideal physique, and significantly aid in their recovery. Understanding soccer positions will help you determine if a specific role is well-suited for your skills. It is important to know that there are additional types of specific positions—not just forwards, midfielders, and defenders. A former or current professional player in the same position as you can provide guidance on the requirements to effectively play that position.

Finally, you must develop a mindset that will leave you unshakable. This mindset will help you prepare for game situations, learn how to deal with other players, and be mentally tough enough to not worry about circumstances that you cannot control, such as the type of field you play on, the officiating, or the weather.

The pyramid is a great visual aid to consider when choosing what areas to focus on next as a soccer player, coach, or parent. However, remember that a team's pyramid may look slightly different based on which tactics the players can handle and which approach the coach decides to use for games. Now that you know where this book plays into the bigger picture, let us begin.

Remember that if there are any words or terms whose meaning you are unsure of; you can feel free to reference the glossary at the back of the book. **Finally, if you enjoy this book, please leave a review on Amazon letting me know.**

Soccer Mindset:

A Step-by-Step Guide on How to Outsmart Your Opponents and Improve Your Mentality

Chapter 1

Growth Mindset vs. Fixed Mindset

Philosopher William James has stated, "The greatest discovery of my generation is that a human being can alter his life by altering his *attitudes*." Essentially, a person's mindset as they experience events, as well as how they reflect upon them afterward, is a key indicator of how quickly that person will grow. One of the best things to help you grow in in soccer and life is understanding the difference between a fixed mindset and a growth mindset.

The fixed mindset is that of someone who believes their basic qualities of intelligence, talent, humor, athletic ability, etc. are fixed traits. Those with fixed mindsets find areas where they can show how great they are versus looking for opportunities that are humbling and will allow them to grow. Also, people with fixed mindsets tend to rely on talent for their success. For example, a fixed mindset for a soccer player is believing they have a fixed trait about how hard they can shoot a soccer ball.

On the other hand, a person with a growth mindset knows that their basic qualities of intelligence, talent, humor, athletic ability, etc. are just abilities they have

developed over time, using knowledge and hard work. People with growth mindsets look for opportunities slightly outside their comfort zone to grow from the new experiences. They understand certain people are more suited for certain jobs, roles, or positions in life. They know that with focused effort, they can change their basic qualities and rely on hard work, along with continuous learning to ensure a life of growth. For example, a growth mindset for a soccer player is believing they can improve how hard they can shoot by lifting weights to gain muscle, reading about what is good shooting form, finding a trainer to guide them on abilities, and practicing to become a much more powerful shooter.

Generally, people are not in a 100% fixed mindset or a 100% growth mindset. They are somewhere between these two ends of the spectrum. The trick is to direct yourself towards the growth mindset. Here are some examples of fixed mindset (FM) phrases and growth mindset (GM) phrases:

FM: I am a failure because I did not do well in a soccer game.
GM: I may have failed in the game but if I work harder, I will become better and succeed next time.

FM: I am doing this because I want to look smart.
GM: I am doing this because I want a challenge.

FM: I did well because I am talented.

GM: I did well because I am a hard worker, and I am applying what I am learning.

FM: They did well because they were lucky.

GM: They did well because they made their own luck.

A fault with the human mind is the need to appear consistent. Many people value consistency over growth and learning what is right. Take a minute and think about a relative you have—maybe an aunt or uncle who is always telling everyone "how it really is." Possibly, you have a parent who gets into arguments and occasional shouting matches when someone disagrees with them. Maybe you have a son or daughter who does not like to attempt new things but cannot verbalize and tell you why, other than because "they just don't like trying new things." People like this want to appear consistent in everything they do, they avoid new experiences outside their comfort zone, and they find fault in others without realizing they have many faults themselves. These are the same people who need to look smart in the short-run, which almost always ensures they do not look smart in the long-run.

Remember that anyone can change, but often it is the person with a growth mindset who will. Personally, I used to have a fixed mindset. After reading many books, I realized it was holding me back tremendously. Malcolm Gladwell, a three-time New York Best-Selling author in the field of personal development, points out that our society prefers effortless successes than a person having to struggle to succeed. This is so true but also very sad because talent is not something to control but learning and working hard are controllable.

An example of a person who fell into the trap of a fixed mindset is Freddy Adu. Adu made world news when he was DC United's first pick in the MLS Super Draft in 2004. Amazingly, he was only 14 years old. The attacking midfielder soon was compared to Pelé, one of the greatest soccer players of all-time. Yes, before Adu even set foot on a professional field, he was already receiving the hype reserved only for those players who had already proven themselves. Sadly, Adu did not live up to many Americans' hopes for a world-class soccer player whom we could call our own. He played for 12 clubs in eight different countries over his career and made little difference at each of the clubs he joined.

His early successes, before the age of 14, were often said to come from his natural abilities. The problem was that he could not improve his natural abilities. Those were things he either had or did not have. The constant praise during Adu's childhood likely resulted in a very fixed mindset. Carol S. Dweck, Ph.D. in her famous book, *Mindset*, revealed that when children are praised for their intelligence and natural abilities rather than for their ability to work hard, their motivation to take on challenges drops and their performances on later tasks diminishes significantly. If you have a son or daughter and want to ensure they grow up without the limiting beliefs that a person with a fixed mindset has, consider grabbing the *Understand Soccer* series book, *Soccer Parenting,* for a step-by-step guide on growing your child's self-esteem and abilities in soccer and in life.

Even if you make mistakes, remind yourself to distinguish the difference between learning and failing. **Failing is when you mess up and give up without learning.** Many of the most successful people in the world have made more mistakes than anyone else, but they never stopped working toward their dreams. Remember, you have only truly failed once you have given up.

YouTube: If you would like to see a video on the difference between the growth and fixed mindset, then watch the *Understand Soccer* YouTube video: *Growth vs. Fixed Mindset*.

Chapter 2

Challenging vs. Threatening

Imagine you have two games this upcoming weekend. Before the first game, your parent tells you, "This game will be a great challenge. It will test what you are made of and will take lots of effort. I am excited for you to compete tomorrow." Come game time, you are alert and excited to play. Your body is releasing adrenaline, and you are ready to rock! You do your best and contribute to your team's victory. Terrific!

Before the second game that weekend, the same parent has another conversation with you. They say, "The other team is coming for your team. Even though you guys were in first place all season, your opponent tomorrow could really threaten your team's chance of winning the championship." Just before the start of the game, you seem nervous and tense. Your body is releasing the stress hormone cortisol and you want to be anywhere but on the field.

When confronted with the same game of soccer against two teams that were relatively similar in talent, you responded differently based on conversations you had before each game. The conversation before the first game, you were told, "The game will be a great challenge. It will test what you are made of and will take lots of effort. I am excited for you in the competition tomorrow." However, before the second game, your parent stated, "The other team is coming for your team. Even though you guys were in first place all season, your opponent tomorrow could really threaten your team's chance of winning the championship."

At first glance, these seem like two very similar conversations with your parent who was showing support and love. With both conversations, your parent believed they were helping steer you towards victory. However, if you look a little deeper, you will notice each of the talks changed how you were feeling on the field to start the game. Though there are more factors that can play a role like your personality and views on how things work, notice that for the first game, your parent referenced the game as a challenge. Before the second game, your parent referenced it as a threat.

In psychology, these are referred to as a "gain" (i.e., a challenge) and a "loss-prevention" (i.e., a threat). Understanding the difference between a challenge and a threat can be a huge factor in your success. Viewing a competition as a challenge means you can gain from it by winning, and there is nothing to lose. Viewing the competition as a threat means you have *everything* to lose. Go back and reread the first section of this chapter and see if you can now point out the differences between what was said before your first and second games.

As an example, in the 2019 Champions League semifinals, Barcelona took a commanding lead in the two-game competition by winning the first game at their home field, Camp Nou, by a score of 3-0. Liverpool would need to score four goals without conceding any goals in the second game at Liverpool's stadium, Anfield, to go to the Champions League final. To make things more difficult, two of the three starting forwards, Salah and Firmino, were out of the game with injuries.

Barcelona was threatened because they had everything to lose. It would be a huge challenge for Liverpool to score 4 goals against one of the greatest clubs of all-time, but the two backups did not see it that way. They realized they were expected to lose and loved the challenge. Sure enough, Divock Origi and Georginio Wijnaldum each scored two goals to lead their team to the 4-0 victory they needed to advance to the Champions League final. It was unbelievable and largely because these two men took it as a challenge to beat the seemingly unbeatable odds, even though they were two unknown backups.

Given how surprising this was, many people could not believe this happened nor would happen again. However, the next night in the other Champions League semifinal match, Ajax was leading the Tottenham Hotspurs 2-0 at halftime and 3-0 overall because of their 1-0 win in the first game at their home stadium, Johan Cruijff Arena. Forward Lucas Moura of the Tottenham Hotspurs realized they needed 3 goals to advance to the finals (due to away goals) and had only 45 minutes to do it, while needing to avoid conceding more goals to Ajax.

Ajax team members were threatened at this point because they had everything to lose in the second half. Sure enough, Lucas Moura realized his side had nothing to lose and scored three second half goals to lift his side to their first Champions League final ever. Two of the most unbelievable Champions League semifinal games of all-time were played on back-to-back nights and highlighted the difference in viewing a soccer game as a challenge versus viewing the opposition as a threat. Now, let us consider a few ways to ensure you are being challenged and not threatened:

1. The first thing to consider takes no effort on your part. The scoring in soccer is already additive, meaning that each time your team scores, you are rewarded with a goal on the scoreboard. Many students have trouble with school because of the subtractive nature of homework assignments. Specifically, many students believe they start an assignment or test with a 100%, and each wrong answer takes away points. **Counting**

upwards instead will not eliminate stress about performance, but it will place students in a "gain" mindset rather than a "loss-prevention" mindset.

2. Anson Dorrance, the coach of the University of North Carolina Women's Soccer Team, has won 22 national titles and achieved the ranking of Sixth-Best Sports Dynasty of All-Time by Beckett Entertainment. When Dorrance's team went up by a point or two, they refused to shift their attitude towards defense. They did not want to protect a lead (i.e., cultivate a "threat" attitude). Instead, they wanted to score more (i.e., maintain a "challenge" attitude). By attacking a challenge, you will develop the skills needed to remain in this frame of mind. **Therefore, it is important to understand that you should never let up on an opponent.**

This concept may offend some people, but during seasons and tournaments when goal differentials can determine who wins the championship, it is important to always keep the "challenge" attitude and keep scoring. For example, consider the United States Women's National Team in the 2019 World Cup. In their first match, they played Thailand. At halftime, they had a convincing 3-0 lead, which would have been more than enough, considering Thailand was a low-ranked opponent, and the U.S. team was ranked #1 in the world. However, did the U.S. team coast for the rest of the game? Nope, they scored 10 more goals in the second half to win by a final score of 13-0. Again, letting up is not the mindset you want to have.

3. **Ask yourself before a match which mindset you are currently in.** You do not need to tell anyone else that you are doing it. Simply ask yourself, "Do I have a 'challenge' mindset right now, or a 'threat' mindset?" It is often difficult for you to realize in a match which way you are thinking if you have not been trained to do so. When you make sure you are in a 'challenge' mindset, you will win many more games during your career.

4. **Avoid using guilt or threats to motivate yourself to perform better.** While threats may help provide short-term results, the long-term costs of the emotional damage may be too much for you to overcome. Using fear as a motivator takes the fun out of playing soccer. A "threat" conveys the message that you do not believe you can do it, whereas a "challenge" says that you believe you *can* do it. Therefore, do not say things to yourself like, "I will not be able to play with my friends", or "I will be in a bad mood for the rest of the day." Also, avoid statements of guilt like, "My family spent a lot of time and money for me to be here; I cannot let them down." If thoughts like those enter your mind, dismiss them. Instead, tell yourself this is a challenge you will overcome.

Understanding the difference between the challenged and threatened attitudes can make it easier to perform. Remember that each practice and game is a challenge, so avoid using guilt to motivate yourself. Though it may work in the short-term, it often results in stagnant growth in the long-term. Lastly, do not expect yourself to be perfect all at once. **It takes time and many games for the lessons and techniques described in this book to impact your soccer game positively.** If this chapter seems familiar, there is a similar chapter in the book, *Soccer Parenting*. Therefore, if you are a soccer parent reading this book, order a copy of the *Understand Soccer* series book, *Soccer Parenting,* to learn many things, including how to give feedback effectively to your child, how to work with the coach to ensure success for your child, and the top 10 things every soccer player needs to hear from their parent.

Since viewing the game as a challenge instead of a threat is one way to help reduce anxiety before a game, let us discuss a few other ways to reduce it. Some symptoms of performance anxiety include:

1. Racing heart rate
2. Rapid breathing
3. Dry mouth
4. Tight throat
5. Trembling hands, knees, and voice
6. Sweaty hands

7. Cold hands
8. Nausea
9. An uneasy feeling of butterflies in your stomach
10. Restlessness

Some ways to overcome anxiety before a match are:

1. **Recognize that pre-game jitters are normal.** Accept the nervous energy you feel and reframe it as excitement rather than nerves. This topic is discussed in great detail in the *Understand Soccer* series book, *Soccer Tryouts,* as most people feel more nervousness before a tryout than before an important game. Avoid misinterpreting the excitement you feel before the game as fear. The adrenaline rush you experience is your body's way of getting you ready for game time. Understand its importance but avoid focusing on it. Once the match starts, the feeling will go away after a few minutes, and you will instead become focused on what you must do in the game.

2. **Prepare both mentally and physically.** Arrive at the game with plenty of time, so you are not rushed. Ensure you do a complete warm-up involving dynamic stretching so that your body is physically ready to perform. Worry and confidence are at opposite ends of the spectrum. When confidence is strong, it tends to push worry out of the mind, so control what you can before the game to ensure confidence *during* the game.

3. **Visualize your performance.** Mentally rehearsing the likely game scenarios that you will come across will reduce your level of anxiety when you find yourself in those situations.

4. **Consider deep breathing.** This can be done alongside visualization and needs to be practiced to become effective. Taking full breaths through your nose while expanding your stomach (not your chest or upper back) will help release tension from your body and mind.

5. **Distract yourself.** Distracting yourself prior to the game could involve doing homework, listening to music, joking around with teammates, reading a book, watching motivational videos on YouTube, looking at memes, or browsing inspirational pictures. All these activities can prevent your mind from generating negative thoughts about the game. Memes are one way I distract myself, if needed. If memes are something you enjoy too, be sure to follow me on Instagram **@UnderstandSoccer** for fun soccer facts, as well as a ton of soccer memes!

YouTube: If you would like to learn about challenges versus threats in a video format, then watch the *Understand Soccer* YouTube video: *How to Have More Fun Playing Soccer*.

Chapter 3

Locus of Control

For the context of this book, the "locus of control" is a term used in modern psychology to show how much a person believes they can control the outcomes of events in their lives. **Specifically, a soccer player with an external locus of control believes that external circumstances like the weather, teammates' opinions, and what past coaches have taught are what shapes their future. Whereas a soccer player with an internal locus of control believes their own work ethic, perseverance, mindset, attitude, and feelings are ultimately what determine their future.**

An external locus of control places the blame on circumstances you cannot control. It will leave you feeling like there is nothing you can do to make your current situation better and that "it is what it is." **Whereas, the internal locus of control mindset allows you to learn from your present situation, work to improve what you already have, and overcome obstacles that are placed in front of you.**

In the chapter on the fixed mindset versus the growth mindset, we pointed out Freddy Adu. Freddy Adu had an external locus of control, which is very often paired with the fixed mindset. By seeing his skills as being gifted to him (i.e., given to him by outside forces), he had an external locus of control and believed that it will happen if it is meant to be.

A player who embodies the opposite of this is Lionel Messi, the forward for Barcelona and Argentina, who is one of the greatest players of all-time. He has an internal locus of control knowing that his abilities were developed over time. Granted, many people view him as gifted and Cristiano Ronaldo, a winger for Manchester United/Real Madrid/Juventus and Portugal, as having to work for everything. However, if you look at their backgrounds, they come from very similar situations and have very similar attitudes of wanting to be the one in control. Throughout their careers, they wanted to determine the outcome of games for their team. In fact, the following quote by Lionel Messi reveals that he worked hard to become a success. He stated, "It took me 17 years and 114 days to become an overnight success." This quote reveals that he knows there is no such thing as an overnight success. He believes in controlling his circumstances and working hard to be the best he can be. **Similarly, he constantly strives to beat his previous self and become even better with each passing year.**

One of the many tricks Messi uses is to control more things leading up to the game. **Many players have very long routines the day before games and the day of games to**

increase their control over their process and ensure they can perform at their peak come game time. Although Messi's routine is extensive, let us break down his meal preparation, according to *Men's Health Magazine*.

A week before a match, Messi decreases his carbohydrate intake and increases the amount of protein and water he consumes. Also, Lionel Messi eats vegetable soup with spices at the beginning of meals. Some spices Messi uses are chili powder, coriander, ginger, and turmeric. Chili powder helps prevent inflammation, increases blood flow, and burns fat. Coriander helps prevent inflammation, fights infection, and boosts memory. Ginger helps prevent inflammation, reduces pain, improves digestion, and increases cardiovascular health. Turmeric helps prevent inflammation, delays aging, aids digestion, and reduces pain.

Without as many carbohydrates, Messi may experience slightly less energy in the days leading up to a game. Cutting carbohydrates forces his body to become more efficient with the sugar levels in his blood. Once Messi reintroduces the carbohydrates a day before the game and the day of the game, it increases his energy because of the carb loading. Messi's ideal dinner the day before a game has meat (e.g., fish, chicken, or prawns), green veggies, an orange, and potatoes. Six hours before match time, Messi eats porridge and egg whites. Then,

90 minutes before the game starts, Messi eats fruit. Now, do you need to go to this extent by starting a week before each game to see results? Probably not but understanding that the more you increase your locus of control and the more you feel your control will increase your confidence and performance on the field.

If you are interested in learning more about proper soccer nutrition to ensure you have the energy to perform amazingly in every single game, then consider grabbing the *Understand Soccer* series book, *Soccer Nutrition*. This book breaks down the meal plans of soccer's greats, reveals the keys to pre-game and post-game nutrition, and discusses the few things that make the biggest impact if you are wanting the most out of your meal plan for your time and money.

In conclusion, remember that taking responsibility for everything you can take responsibility for may be slightly overwhelming at first. **However, it will be a relief in the long run, because if you are responsible for it, then that means you can change it.** The most tiring and emotionally exhausting things are those you cannot control. By increasing your locus of control, you will decrease the things that drain your mental and physical energy.

Activity: Locus of Control

For each of the following statements, pick the option you most agree with to see where you sit on the locus of control spectrum. The answers are in the appendix at the end of the book.

A. It is too hard to be good at soccer these days.
B. I know it is up to me to become good at soccer.

A. Joining a good soccer team depends on being in the right place at the right time and knowing the right people.
B. Becoming a success in soccer is a matter of hard work; luck has little or nothing to do with it.

A. What happens to me in soccer is my own doing.
B. Sometimes, I feel that I do not have enough control over the direction my soccer career is taking.

A. In the long run, people receive the respect they deserve in soccer.
B. Unfortunately, an individual's worth in soccer often passes unrecognized, no matter how hard they try.

A. The coach is the major factor in how well I play for a team.
B. I have the greatest control over how I play for a team.

A. Without the right breaks, one cannot be an effective coach of a soccer team.

B. Capable people who fail to become good coaches have not yet taken advantage of their opportunities.

A. Players who cannot get along with other players do not understand how to get along with others.

B. No matter how hard you try; some teammates will not like you.

A. When I make plans in soccer, I am almost always certain that they will work.

B. It is not always wise to plan too far ahead in soccer because many things turn out to be a matter of luck anyway.

Chapter 4

Identity Capital

Identity capital is our collection of mental assets. These are the skills, thought processes, mindsets, and resourcefulness we assemble over time. Additionally, it is how we solve problems, how well we can speak to others, and, to an extent, even how we look. Ideally, these are developed over the course of your entire life and are built moment-by-moment with each new experience. However, most people still have not developed these abilities after their traditional schooling has finished.

Traditional schooling is meant to lay the groundwork and provide the basics for having a fulfilling life. **After your traditional schooling is completed, it is up to you to keep building on the framework set in place by your years in elementary, middle, and high school.** Granted, some people attend college or a university, but this basically provides specific knowledge in your major, without providing many of the real-world skills that everyday people need to succeed on their own terms.

To be completely honest, I lacked identity capital as a child. I was very self-conscious and unconfident. In soccer games, the only time I performed well was when I believed I was the best player on the soccer team. If there were other children who were better than me, I would shut down in fear and not play to my abilities because I thought they were better and should lead the team.

To make matters worse, I had tons of excuses for anything that did not go my way. There was always something or someone else for me to blame. After years of listening to a soccer mentor on how to play well and reading many books to improve my communication abilities, increase my confidence, and decrease my fear of failure, I can now enjoy soccer and contribute to the team even if I am not the best player on the team. I take on challenges that scare me but will ultimately help me grow and build my identity capital.

People who go through an identity crisis often will say things like, "I need to find myself." Whereas, people who focus less on a crisis in their own head and focus on building up their identity capital will say things like, "I need to create myself." Yes, this implies you will need to work to create yourself. Excitingly, you will be building yourself in a way you have chosen which ensures it will feel less like work and more like play.

When I first started writing soccer books, it felt like work because there was so much to learn and a lot of things to do. However, after I built identity capital as an author, writing seemed less like work. Now, writing is my way of helping soccer players improve their confidence and individual skills, and this is what I have consciously chosen to build my identity capital around. It is something I enjoy doing daily and even though parts of it can be exhausting, it is very rewarding to see my skills as an author grow as I help soccer players like you in ways I really needed help with when I was your age.

In terms of soccer, never building up the identity capital by playing on teams slightly outside your comfort zone, being the person to demonstrate drills with your coach while not worrying if you make a mistake, and never working towards your desired position on the soccer field can lead to having to confront some harsh truths. You will notice an increase in your sadness, you will probably question if you like soccer, and will have a nagging thought in the back of your mind telling you to quit playing soccer because you are not good enough. Taking the steps to avoid these unproductive thoughts is how you build your identity capital.

Therefore, when selecting a team to join or a position to play in soccer, pick the one that will provide the most identity capital. Pick the team where you will build the best relationships, learn a lot of techniques, and grow the most. Pick the position you can see yourself playing for many years to come and the one that seems the most fun to you. **Do not worry if you have all the skills necessary right this moment. Just make sure you do not give up learning and growing to ensure you will become great at the position you want on your team of choice.**

Avoid picking a team that is the most prestigious if it means you will sit on the bench the whole season. Being a benchwarmer means you will not be obtaining much in-game experience. However, you do not want to join a team where you are clearly the best because then you will probably practice/play with sub-par competition and will not grow like you would if you played against soccer players who are slightly better than you.

Here are 10 ways for you to boost your soccer identity capital immediately:

1. Build more experience on the field by playing with older kids and better kids, while not being afraid to make mistakes;
2. Identify the goals you want to achieve in the next month, season, year, and five years;
3. Ask your coach for more responsibility on your team;
4. Read soccer books to gain knowledge;

5. Avoid comparing yourself to others; instead, only compare yourself to your previous self;

6. Make it a habit to practice for at least 30 minutes per day, six days per week;

7. Analyze the play style of the soccer players you admire to learn from them;

8. Watch interviews of the soccer players you admire to better understand their mindset;

9. Befriend your coach to increase your communication skills and time on the field; and

10. Do what you fear most in soccer.

In conclusion, there is not just one thing you must do to ensure you will have all the identity capital you will ever need. Playing time and quality training are needed to improve and build your skills. **Once your abilities are built, they are very easy to maintain and are easier to build even further.** Similar to when you first started playing soccer, the beginning is the toughest part because you have so much to learn and so many skills to develop. However, as you begin to add skills and abilities, it becomes easier and fun to add more!

Chapter 5

The Comfort Zone Trap

Many soccer players, coaches, and parents fall into the trap of the comfort zone. I am not perfect either and I fall into the comfort zone trap on occasion, too. However, it is important to understand what it means to stay there. Learning the importance of traveling outside your comfort zone will make it increasingly easier for you to grow. Therefore, let us start by looking at the different zones you will travel through as you go from your comfort zone to your growth zone.

As you can see in the image, your goal is to go from the comfort zone through the fear and learning zones to arrive at the growth zone. Sure, the comfort zone feels safe because you feel in control of your surroundings and the things you are working on. **However, the comfort zone is not ideal because when you are comfortable, your learning slows or stops altogether.** Taking a step outside your comfort zone puts you in the fear zone, which is also known as the "terror barrier."

In the fear zone, you realize that you will need to learn skills to arrive at the growth zone. The fear zone is often where someone lets other peoples' opinions affect their thoughts. Most people will attempt something new to step out of their comfort zone. The problem is that they do not realize they are the most vulnerable and have the lowest self-confidence immediately outside of their comfort zone. **Sadly, most people will create excuses and reasons that whatever they are attempting to do is too difficult and they will go back to their comfort zone feeling upset and defeated.**

Excitingly, as the person reading this, you now understand that you can go back to your comfort zone after stepping into the fear zone, but the trick is to learn more. **You have low self-esteem in the fear zone because you do not yet know enough about what you are attempting to do.** However, learning what to do, whether that be from your own mistakes or by someone else's mistakes, will allow you to enter the learning zone.

In the learning zone, you will pick up the skills and abilities needed to overcome your problems and challenges. **For soccer players, you can learn from reading, a coach/parent, watching soccer, watching "how to" videos about soccer on YouTube, and from attempting something yourself to figure out how to improve.** The learning zone requires you to put in work, but it is the last step before achieving your goal in the growth zone.

Finally, after having learned and implemented what you needed, you arrive in the growth zone. The growth zone is an exciting place to be because it is where your dreams in soccer become reality. It allows you to be okay with making mistakes because you know you will contribute to your team's success every single game. In this zone, you will experience some level of anxiety, but you can turn it into motivation and fuel for productivity. **By learning to overcome your fears, you will feel great. You will love playing soccer, and your enjoyment of it will keep growing.**

Now that you understand how to travel to the growth zone (also known as your "stretch zone"), you can begin to expand the things you are comfortable doing because your growth zone will eventually turn into your comfort zone. Sadly, you must not go too fast, or you risk going past the growth zone and into what is known as the "panic zone", a term coined by Andy Molinsky, an author, researcher, and the Professor of Organizational Behavior at Brandeis University's International Business School.

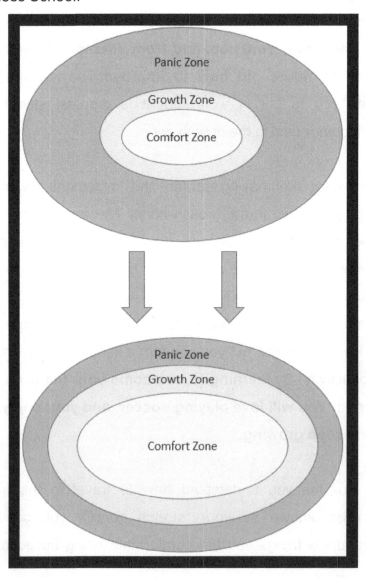

As you can see in the image, the panic zone (also known as the snap zone) is where you will end up if you are taking on too much and not allowing enough time to recover from the anxiety and stress often associated with growing. Therefore, the threshold of anxiety overtakes your capacity to handle the stress. You can often see the panic zone with your teammates or even in yourself because you all work so hard to be better but mentally burn out and often obtain physical injuries. **As you grow in your comfort zone, the potential things that can sap your energy and cause you stress decreases.**

An example of moving to the growth zone is when you realize you want to beat a defender 1v1 as the defender is backpedaling towards their net. You attempt to dribble past them, get stopped, and now become fearful that you will never be able to dribble past the defender. Then, you remember that you must improve your knowledge and skills to overcome that fear and understand what it takes. As you learn new abilities, you practice them on defenders. For the first several tries, you still cannot beat a defender 1v1. Still, you keep your head held high because you realize you can learn a ton from your mistakes. **You mentally go over what went wrong, change it, and finally learn to beat a defender 1v1 almost every time.** This is great because you have entered the growth zone.

At this point, you are excited to see that moving from your comfort zone to your growth zone is a learnable process. Now that you have arrived at the growth zone, you say to yourself, "Instead of just learning one skill and focusing on using it right now, I am going to focus on five of them at once." You attempt to learn the shot fake, the self-pass, the step over, shooting a driven shot with precise form, and passing correctly using the inside of your foot. You attempt to learn what you need for each one at the same time and realize you are not spending enough time on any of them individually. You burn out and distance yourself from learning these new skills. Sadly, you find yourself not as excited about soccer as you were when you were learning just one thing thoroughly. **Learning five things at once and not going very in-depth in one thing is how you enter the panic zone and stunt your growth.**

It is important that when you enter the growth zone, you avoid the panic zone. You must avoid depleting all your emotional capital by doing too many things at once without the recovery and rest/sleep needed for a soccer player to succeed. If you are interested in a great night's sleep every single night to help your body and mind recover, then grab the *Understand Soccer* series book, *Soccer Sleep*. Once you master a skill, then move on to the next one.

In conclusion, the growth zone eventually turns into the comfort zone because as you grow and learn new things, they become increasingly comfortable for you. **If you are thinking to yourself, "It seems like it is a lot of work to become better," then consider that to be a good thing.** If it were easy, everyone would do it! Therefore, since there is some hard work ahead of you, you will quickly become better than your opponents and even the other players on your team! If you do not do this, you can still enjoy soccer, but you will lose out on the continual growth that someone else on your team will gain.

You can further your growth by reading books in the *Understand Soccer* series, practicing the skills you read about, learning from your mistakes, and becoming a continual learner of this beautiful game. It is great to know that, as you go on the journey of continued improvement, you will realize that things seem to become easier. However, it is not that things are becoming easier; it is just that *you are becoming better*.

Chapter 6

Compounding Skills

In finance, there are two terms that describe how your bank savings account could grow in value: **(1) compound interest; and (2) simple interest.** These are fancy terms for an easy concept. "Simple interest" is how most people think of the effort they give in soccer. Let us say you are just starting your soccer career and have not yet worked to improve your soccer skills at all. In this case, you are starting with zero strengths. (If you play FIFA, you can also think of strengths as the "talent points" that you use to upgrade your attributes.) If you are starting at zero strengths, then you must deliberately practice, which means you must learn and work hard to gain five strengths from practice. Therefore, "simple interest" means every time you train and enhance your skills, you obtain exactly five more strengths. Therefore, if you train seven times, you gain 5+5+5+5+5+5+5 strengths (or 35 total strengths). The following image shows the simple interest of your strengths:

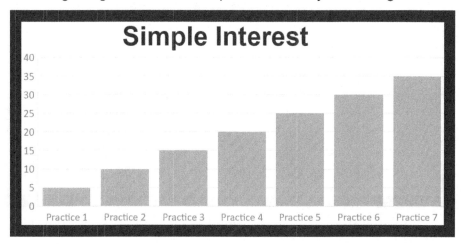

How soccer (and your bank savings account) actually work is through compound interest. Consider that you are starting at zero strengths, and you practice seven times. However, because strengths compound, you gain five strengths from the first practice. You can now invest all those extra strengths into your next practice. Instead of gaining another five strengths (as shown in the simple interest concept), you gain six strengths from your second practice. Now, you are at 11 strengths, and you can use them in your next practice, from which you will gain eight strengths. After your third practice, you are now up to 19 strengths.

Your strengths keep compounding with each additional practice, so you gain 10 strengths in your fourth practice, 13 strengths in your fifth practice, 16 strengths in your sixth practice, and 20 strengths in your seventh practice.

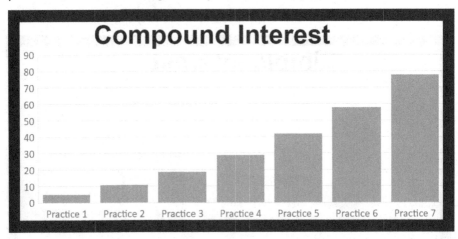

Remember that from simple interest, you gained five strengths each practice and went from zero strengths to 35 strengths after seven practices. However, compound interest shows us that we gained a total of 78 strengths (5+6+8+10+13+16+20) from the seven deliberate practices. This is more than double the 35 strengths gained from the simple interest example. **Therefore, by obtaining soccer skills and proper techniques, and then deliberately practicing them, you will grow your strengths quicker than most people realize.**

Think about how it is much easier to learn a bicycle (overhead) kick for a soccer player who can shoot well, correctly time a ball in the air, and has good jumping abilities than it is for a new soccer player who cannot do any of those things yet. **Therefore, your skills and abilities compound on top of each other.**

A similar term related to soccer is "never miss a cone." Too many trainees do not realize that missing one cone each lap for a four-lap drill is four cones missed. Add those missed cones up over the course of the training session, and they equate to roughly 40 missed cones. Add that up over an 8-week course, and that is 320 cones missed. Add that up over an entire career, and the soccer player who skips cones is missing up to 30,000 or so opportunities to become better. Remember that you are already spending time training, so you might as well make the most of it. Missing one additional rep each lap does not seem like much in the moment, but it surely prevents you from compounding the skills that will make you better more quickly.

Also, remember that when you do not practice, you lose your strengths. **You are either becoming better or becoming worse; there is no such thing as keeping your strengths exactly the same.** For every 3-4 days that you rest and do not learn or develop your soccer skills, you can expect to lose strengths. After not practicing for a long weekend, you will often notice that you cannot run for as long without becoming tired, and your foot skills are slightly worse than they were only a few days ago.

Some ways to gain strengths are:

1. Read or listen to books on how to become better at soccer;
2. Learn from your coach(es) or parent(s);
3. Learn from a teammate's advice after you made a mistake;
4. Learn from your own mistakes at practice and in games;
5. Watch the world's best soccer players on television; and
6. Watch "how-to" soccer videos on YouTube, such as on the *Understand Soccer* channel.

Compounding your skills, speed, strength, knowledge, confidence, etc. is very important. **Learning about more things and implementing them will create a huge change in you.** After all, bad players take little seriously. Average players take games seriously. Good players take practice and games seriously. Great players take learning, nutrition, sleep, warm-ups, independent work, weight training, conditioning, flexibility, practice, and games seriously.

Above all, remember that some things are more important than others, and there is not enough time to do everything. If the concept of compound interest excites you, check out Jeff Olson's book, *The Slight Edge*. This is a life-changing book. It teaches how, by doing small things—ones that are easy to do but also easy *not* to do—you can forever change your future and have a life full of success.

Chapter 7

Setting S.M.A.R.T Goals Using Step Ladders

The Merriam-Webster Dictionary defines a goal as "the end towards which effort is directed." Determining the goals that you want to achieve as a soccer player will go a long way to help you become a much better soccer player than your teammates and/or opponents who do not set goals. **Generally, all goals you set for yourself should be written down and S.M.A.R.T.**

S.M.A.R.T. stands for:

S = Specific (who what where)

M = Measurable (weigh)

A = Attainable (which)

R = Relevant (why)

T = Timely (when)

S.M.A.R.T. Goal #1: Specific

Your goal must be **specific**. Otherwise, you will not focus your efforts to achieve it. When determining whether your goal is specific, you should answer the following three questions:

1. **What do I want to accomplish?** You must first decide what you want to be your goal. For example, learning how to shoot a driven shot for the first time.

2. **Who is involved?** Ideally, you will have a mentor providing the steps for you. You will need to be involved, too, since you want to learn how to shoot a driven shot.

3. **Where must I go to achieve it?** You must figure out where the goal needs to be met. For a soccer player learning a driven shot, this would be on a soccer field, in your backyard, or on a street without cars.

S.M.A.R.T. Goal #2: Measurable

Your goal must be **measurable**. If you cannot measure it, then it will be hard to determine whether you are becoming better or if you have achieved the goal. Therefore, you must weigh your goal. Weighing something is a method of measurement. A soccer player learning how to shoot a driven shot can measure each step of the process by how many goals they can score in practices and games. Also, you can measure it by the increased power and accuracy in practices.

S.M.A.R.T. Goal #3: Attainable

Your goal must be **attainable**. Learning how to shoot a driven shot is very attainable. However, having a goal to score

100 goals in a single game is not. Make sure you set your sights on something that can be achieved or is slightly past what you think you can achieve. This requires that you ask yourself how you can attain it. For example, learning the steps and spending several practices using deliberate practice to learn how to shoot a driven shot will allow you to score more goals in seemingly no time.

S.M.A.R.T. Goal #4: Relevant

Your goal must be **relevant**. To determine whether your goal is relevant, ask yourself why this goal is important to you. If your aim is to become a better soccer player, then learning how to shoot a driven shot is very relevant, as it will increase the number of goals you score in a season.

S.M.A.R.T. Goal #5: Timely

Your goal must be **timely**. Being able to shoot a driven shot is great but learning it when you are 50-years old and have stopped playing or coaching soccer 20 years ago is not a timely goal. Also, expecting to spend one hour to learn how to shoot with the speed and accuracy of Cristiano Ronaldo is also not timely because that is an unrealistic timeline.

To determine the timeliness of your goal, you must first determine when you need to achieve it. Giving yourself a reasonable deadline will ensure you do not have much time to slack off or too little time to realistically accomplish the goal. A reasonable deadline will ensure you have enough time to accomplish the goal without losing focus.

The Step Ladder Method for Success

Now that you understand S.M.A.R.T. goals, the best way to bring your goals into fruition is to use the "step ladder" method. **Using the step ladder method, a large goal like consistently and powerfully shooting a driven shot can be broken down into parts that are much more manageable.** This is because when using step ladders, the only way to travel to the next step is if you have already taken the one before it.

In the image, you must start at the base of the ladder and master Step One. Then, you can move on to Step Two, and so

6. Ensure Your Hips Are Pointing Where You Want The Ball To Go
5. Make Sure You Bring Your Back Leg Forward
4. Follow Through And Land On Your Shooting Foot
3. Have Your Toe Down And Out While Your Knee Is Facing The Target
2. Plant A Foot Away When The Ball Is Stopped
1. Approach The Ball Diagonally

forth. **However, most soccer players rarely realize that each one of these steps is a building block that you need to lay down to travel to the next step.** If we take the image and look at it from the side instead of from the front, this becomes clearer that it looks more like a staircase:

					6. Ensure Your Hips Are Pointing Where You Want The Ball To Go
				5. Make Sure You Bring Your Back Leg Forward	5. Make Sure You Bring Your Back Leg Forward
			4. Follow Through And Land On Your Shooting Foot	4. Follow Through And Land On Your Shooting Foot	4. Follow Through And Land On Your Shooting Foot
		3. Have Your Toe Down And Out While Your Knee Is Facing The Target	3. Have Your Toe Down And Out While Your Knee Is Facing The Target	3. Have Your Toe Down And Out While Your Knee Is Facing The Target	3. Have Your Toe Down And Out While Your Knee Is Facing The Target
	2. Plant A Foot Away When The Ball Is Stopped	2. Plant A Foot Away When The Ball Is Stopped	2. Plant A Foot Away When The Ball Is Stopped	2. Plant A Foot Away When The Ball Is Stopped	2. Plant A Foot Away When The Ball Is Stopped
1. Approach The Ball Diagonally	1. Approach The Ball Diagonally	1. Approach The Ball Diagonally	1. Approach The Ball Diagonally	1. Approach The Ball Diagonally	1. Approach The Ball Diagonally

As you can see, each step is built upon the previous one. Often, players will only focus on the certain steps they want to learn and avoid spending time on the other steps. However, the previous image shows that each step should only be taken after the previous one has already been mastered. Also, when setting goals, not having actionable steps makes the goal of shooting a driven shot correctly a huge goal. **When you can break it down into its parts, each step seems more manageable and easier to do than if they were all lumped together.**

In the book written by Gary Keller and Jay Papasan, *The One Thing*, this type of goal setting is also referred to as "goal setting to the NOW." **Set a future goal, then drill down to what you should do right now.** If your goal will take roughly one year to accomplish, then figure out what you need to have done six months from now, one month from now, one week from now, by the end of the day, and what you can start right now. In conclusion, using S.M.A.R.T. goals will help you determine exactly which goals you should set for yourself and how to plan the steps to make the goal much easier to achieve.

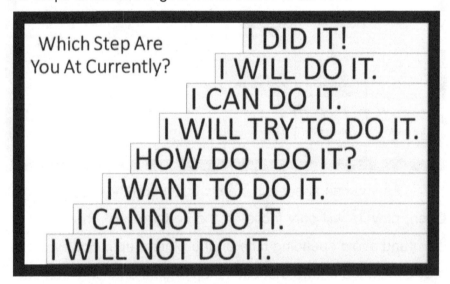

To learn how to score and when to use many of the different types of shots, like the driven shot, grab the *Understand Soccer* series book, *Soccer Shooting & Finishing*.

YouTube: If you would like to learn how to set S.M.A.R.T. soccer goals in a video format, then watch the *Understand Soccer* YouTube video: *How to Set S.M.A.R.T. Goals*.

Chapter 8

Deliberate Practice

Deliberate > Purposeful > Habitual Practice

If you have read the *Understand Soccer* series books, *Soccer Coaching* or *Soccer Parenting,* then this chapter will look similar to the chapter on deliberate practice in those books. However, this book is for the soccer player who is working on the field, so this chapter will describe the soccer player's role to ensure they practice deliberately.

As a soccer player, it is important that you do not just practice to "get touches." There are certain hotspots around the world that produce outstanding performers, like country singers from Tennessee, hockey players from Canada, and soccer players from Brazil. These hotbeds for talent have training programs that involve deliberate practice.

Deliberate practice is systematic. Regular/habitual practice often means dribbling, shooting, and passing in ways you have done before and are comfortable performing. **Deliberate practice requires attention and is accompanied by the specific goal of improving your performance using**

your knowledge of where the practice needs to go and how to travel there step-by-step.

For a soccer player, this is where having a soccer trainer is important. **An experienced soccer trainer will give you the training you need, which will allow you to develop very quickly and deliberately.** However, make sure the soccer trainer is teaching the specifics on how to do things. If you are just dribbling through cones, passing, shooting, and it appears you are just "getting touches" without really learning how to do everything with proper form, then this is likely a trainer to stay away from. Expect measurable progress in a reasonable period of time for yourself. Think about it: by having an in-person or online soccer trainer, they will invest the time and their 20 or so years of knowledge and skill to teach you how to more quickly succeed. Your abilities will skyrocket much quicker than the opponents in your league and even your teammates.

Habitual/regular practice (e.g., trying to juggle) is not as good as purposeful practice (e.g., a player setting a goal for each practice, such as juggling the ball 30 times in a row). Purposeful practice is not as productive as deep and deliberate practice. **Again, deliberate practice is purposeful practice, but it includes the information and knowledge needed to understand how to find your weak areas and improve them.** The goal is to advance quickly by progressively focusing on the areas just outside your comfort zone. For example, juggling with the tops of your feet towards your toes 30 times in a row to better settle the ball out of the air.

When you first start playing soccer, everything is new and just going through the reps will be a new experience in which considerable learning will occur. **But if you train on the same things that you are already good at doing, with no meaningful plan to progress, then you will likely overlook small errors and miss opportunities to improve.**

Mindless activity is the enemy of deliberate practice. The danger of practicing the same thing again and again without focusing on making small improvements is that you believe you are becoming better because you are working on your soccer abilities. In reality, you are likely reinforcing habits that have room for improvement and wasting practice time by merely reinforcing those imperfect habits. The natural tendency of the brain is to turn repeated actions into habits. **Deliberate practice breaks the overall process down into parts, allows you to identify your weaknesses, work on different ways to improve those areas, and then brings all the training together to improve quickly.**

As a soccer trainer, one of the biggest areas my trainees struggle with, especially at a young age, is

shooting a driven shot with correct form. At a high level, a trainee must start diagonal to the ball, then plant a foot away from the ball. Next, on the foot the player is striking the ball with, they must have their toe down and out with their knee facing the target, so they can use the bone of their foot. Afterwards, they must follow through, land on their shooting foot, bring their back leg forward, and point their hips where they want to score. This is a lot for anyone to learn if this is the first time they are working through the steps.

Therefore, instead of working on all the steps at once, I have found it is best to start the trainee planted about a foot away from the ball and focus on striking the ball with the bone of their foot. After 10-15 repetitions of becoming comfortable striking with the bone, I will have them take a step to work on correctly planting next to the ball and continuing to strike with the bone of their foot. Then, after another 10-15 repetitions, I will have them work on following through to land past the ball. **The process is to add in one additional step each time until they are comfortable with that level and then adding another step until they are comfortable shooting driven shots with the correct form.**

You may be wondering how Brazil has so many well-developed soccer players. Well, the most popular form of soccer in Brazil is referred to as *"futebol de salão."* This is 5v5 soccer and is oftentimes played on a basketball court. During each game, each player has 6X more touches than they would in the same time span of an 11v11 soccer game. The Professor of Soccer at the University of São Paulo, Emilio Miranda, says it is Brazil's "laboratory of improvisation." **Adding many more touches with little room and/or little time to make decisions forces players to improve their recognition of patterns and learn how to act in many soccer situations.**

As a soccer player, it is important to understand the concept of deliberate practice so that you can advance your skills quickly and productively, now that you have the soccer knowledge to do so. Recognizing that this is one of the best ways to teach someone a task with many steps will also make it easier for you to determine if a coach is good for you.

If you are interested in learning more about deliberate practice, consider picking up the book *Talent is Overrated* by Geoff Colvin, in which Colvin describes how Benjamin Franklin used deliberate practice to improve his writing skills, and Mozart used deliberate practice to become one of the greatest musicians of all-time at a young age. He confirms the old saying: *"It takes about 10 years and about 10,000 hours of deliberate practice to become an overnight sensation."*

Chapter 9

The 80/20 Rule

The 80/20 principle was first observed by the Italian economist Vilfredo Pareto. As a result, the 80/20 rule is also known as the "Pareto Principle." He first observed it while looking into land ownership in his home country of Italy. His first work on the principle stated that 80% of the land was owned by only 20% of the population. He then looked at many other fields and noticed that the same principle applied. Therefore, the 80/20 rule states that 80% of the results are due to only 20% of the things you do. **In soccer, roughly 20% of your habits have 80% of the impact on your performance.**

Despite this truth, so many players equally weigh everything, both in their minds and in their practices. This is because many soccer players have their priorities in practice backwards. Often, players care more about the cool foot skills and a powerful shot than being able to make a perfect 10-yard pass to the correct foot, lead your teammate making a run, or receive a pass with one touch that perfectly sets you up to take a shot. I will be completely honest when I say I fell into this trap in my early high school soccer years, as well. The things I practiced the most were my shot with the ball stopped, tons of foot skills without being able to use any of them in a real game situation, making sure I had terrific nutrition, and I weight trained 5-6 days per week. Sadly, because I could not effectively receive a pass near the net or dribble past an opposing player, I hardly ever had the opportunity to take a shot.

Let us consider a former teammate of mine, Joey Tinnion, who was a forward for a Division 1 university soccer team, played for the professional team Waza Flo Pro, and is now the coach of a college soccer team. Joey was an all-state forward who scored nearly 30 goals in his junior season of high school. During halftime at one of our high school matches, he told me he practiced the same few skills over and over again, and they seemed to always work. I should have been more intelligent and realized that what he said was outstanding advice. **If a player only ever uses four foot skills, then you can bet they will become fantastic and very effective with those four skills.**

I was unwise at the time, so I thought his advice was bad because I believed that you should know a ton of skills to be great. I ignored his advice for the next couple of years. I continued practicing body feints, single scissors, double scissors, self-passes, rolls, six different shot fakes, three-directionals, step overs, elasticos, rainbows, etc. I was a "jack of all trades and master of none." Sadly, if you do not master any skills, the skills you attempt in a game will not often work when you use them. **This leads to a ton of frustration for a soccer player who is practicing a ton of hours but is not spending those hours working on the best things.** With his four skills, Joey Tinnion kept scoring. On the other hand, me with my 12+ skills, found it hard to even shoot until I realized that I needed only a few skills to become someone who averaged two goals per game.

Next, let us discuss scoring in soccer. There are many ways to score in soccer, but only a few of the ways will provide the most goals throughout your playing career. **In the following image, notice that 80% of a soccer player's goals on average will come from either the driven shot or the bent shot.** Only 20% of the goals that a soccer player scores on average will come from pass shots, headers, trivelas, toe pokes, bicycle kicks, heel shots, or goals from other body parts. Therefore, most of your time should be spent on perfecting the driven shot and the bent shot.

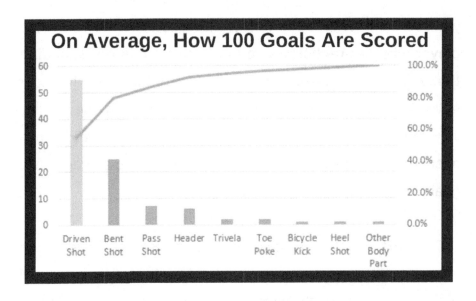

In conclusion, the 80/20 rule states that 80% of your results come from 20% of your actions. Therefore, to become better a lot quicker, you must focus on the few things that will make the biggest impact within the shortest time. Some of these high-impact areas are:

-Passing the ball 10+ yards without error;

-Knowing exactly how to use a moving first touch;

-Learning the Big 3 foot skills;

-Learning how to take a driven shot; and

-Knowing where to push the opposing player while defending.

Working on these few things will help you 10X your game much more quickly than less important things, like being able to juggle the ball 100 times in a row, having a 500-lb deadlift, or stretching for 30 minutes before and after each game.

Additional Reading

If you are curious about the Big 3 foot skills that every soccer player should master for the three main situations you will be in when covered by a defender, then grab the *Understand Soccer* series book, *Soccer Dribbling & Foot Skills*. **This book will teach you how using only three foot skills will make it so you will have plenty of games where you are taking at least 10 shots per game, which almost guarantees you can consistently score two goals per game.** Without knowing what those three skills are or without being able to perform them, you will be like the player I used to be, who lacked the confidence needed on the soccer field.

Additionally, although *Soccer Passing and Receiving* is a terrific guide for players to learn exactly how to pass with correct form and receive the ball to score easily, it is the least-purchased book in the *Understand Soccer* series. Remember that passing and receiving are at the foundation of the "Individual Soccer Player's Pyramid" mentioned in the preface of this book. **If you have read other books in the *Understand Soccer* series but not *Soccer Passing and Receiving*, then you are not following the 80/20 principle.** Instead, you are working on the flashy aspects of soccer without focusing on the major area that will improve your game the quickest.

Passing and receiving are at the base of the "Individual Soccer Player's Pyramid" because it is the foundation that all soccer players need to build an outstanding soccer career. Therefore, I highly suggested you read that book next before going on to any of the other technical books within the "Individual Soccer Player's Pyramid."

YouTube: If you would like to see a video to learn about the 80/20 rule, then watch the *Understand Soccer* YouTube video: *How to Practice Less and Score More*.

Chapter 10

Shooting with Your Opposite Foot

Notice that the title of this chapter says to shoot with your "opposite foot" and not your "weak foot." **By referring to your opposite foot as your weak foot, you are displaying a limiting belief.** If you treat your opposite foot like a weak foot, then you will likely not take the necessary steps to develop it. You will probably avoid practicing with it and avoid developing it to become comfortable using it in a game. How you perceive things in both soccer and in life generally dictates how you will execute and become better. This concept is known as "reframing" and is used by modern psychologists to help people find the silver lining in situations by using constructive words and statements to help people achieve their goals in life.

Most people agree that your beliefs help shape the words you use, but few people realize the opposite is true, too. The words you use help shape your beliefs, which is why you often hear from others that you should "watch what you say." If you are not careful, you might end up believing something that holds you back.

The form for shooting with your opposite foot is the exact same form as shooting with your dominant foot. **Understand**

that you do not need to take a free kick just as good with either foot or that you should be able to shoot from 30 yards out just as easily and accurately with your opposite foot. Being able to shoot with your opposite foot means that if you are inside the 18-yard box, you should be comfortable going to your right foot or to the left foot, whichever foot is going make it easier for you to take a shot. A good defender will attempt to push you to your opposite foot. The opposing defender will give you a bit more space to push the ball, accelerate, and shoot with your opposite foot if you are willing to use it.

Any time I am playing defense, and I am going up against an attacker who only uses one of his feet to shoot the ball, I am very pleased. They are usually easy to shut down, and it takes less effort to prevent them from shooting because you know in which direction they will attempt to go. **All you need to do is give them space towards their opposite foot.** You know they are unlikely to utilize their opposite foot. Even if they do use it, they will not be comfortable enough to take an effective shot. This is why you should make it easy to succeed on the field by developing both of your feet.

Although there are players who have had successful soccer careers using only one foot, such as Mesut Özil, these players are the exception and not the rule. Personally, I did not learn to use my opposite foot until I was 14 years old. As a child and early teenager, I had a lot of limiting beliefs. **One of those limiting beliefs was "I am not naturally gifted at using my opposite foot, so this must mean I should not use it."** Keep in mind that it never registered to me that I was good with my dominant foot only because I used it exclusively for the first 10 years of playing soccer!

Finally, I swallowed my pride and realized that I needed to change. I needed to use my opposite foot. However, I was so ashamed of my form that I was unwilling to use it in a practice or a game.

When I came to this conclusion, it was during a summer when a World Cup was held, as they occur only every four years. I was inspired by the soccer players in those games, and I was still young enough that I had minimal responsibilities outside of soccer. Therefore, every day over the course of that World Cup, I would watch the games and practice shooting for 30 minutes to an hour a day, 4 to 5 times a week with my opposite foot. I would go to the side of my parents' house and work on shooting with my opposite foot. I would either work on shooting for distance/power by striking the ball between my parents' house and my next-door neighbor's house or take shots off the wall of my parents' brick house to work on accuracy. (Note: ask your parents for permission before shooting soccer balls at your home).

For me, it started off very rough. I could not kick the ball with the bone of my foot more than 15-yards and my form was horrible. It felt awkward and I can guarantee you that it looked awkward too. However, I made up my mind that I would keep practicing until I could use my opposite foot. **Notice what was said in the previous sentence. It stated, "I will keep doing it until."** I learned this mindset later in life from the mentor Jim Rohn, who reframed my view on how to approach a task, project, or situation I wanted to attain a certain outcome. Luckily, I intuitively understood it at a young age.

Your mindset is critical because generally, anytime you set out to do something, it will take longer and be more difficult than you originally planned. There are times where a plan you put in place does not work and then you decide to give up. As a result, you still will not be able to use your opposite foot very well because you lacked the mindset and the consistency to keep practicing until you could do what you had initially set your mind to do. Some tips when it comes to shooting with the bone of your opposite foot are:

1. **Make sure you are very angled to the ball (i.e., 45° at the absolute minimum but ideally 60° to 75°).** This is so you can start becoming comfortable with pointing your toe down and out while using the bone of your opposite foot to strike the ball.

2. **Make sure to bend your leg at the hip *and* the knee.** Too many of my trainees only bend at the hip which prevents their strongest muscle, their quadriceps, from being used to increase the power of their shot.

3. **Practice, practice, practice.** Make sure you do enough repetitions so that you will start to develop a consistent form. Clearly, you will want this form to be perfect from the beginning, but if you are uncomfortable shooting with your opposite foot and have not really practiced using it yet, then your first goal is to become more comfortable using your opposite foot to strike the ball. Even if you are worried about your form needing correction, first focus on making it consistent.

A professional player who has a great story about using his opposite foot is David Villa. David Villa had played for Barcelona, Atlético Madrid, and the Spanish National Team but was almost unable to because of an injury he sustained when he was four years old. Villa, who was a right-footed player, suffered a broken right leg. With the guidance of his father to push him to use his left leg, he was able to come back stronger than other players his age because he started off so young being able to use both feet to dribble, pass, and shoot. His ability to use both feet laid the groundwork for a fantastic career as a striker in soccer.

Keep in mind that improvement takes time. If you do not do it correctly right away—or even over the course of a few weeks—then that is okay! Know that it took me about two-and-a-half months to even become comfortable enough to use my opposite foot in practice—and I was *still* uncomfortable even *attempting* an opposite-footed shot in a game! Therefore, if you feel uncomfortable using your opposite foot, then practice using it in your free time, either outside your house, on a soccer field, or on an open piece of land to work on developing an opposite foot that you can rely on to score.

If you want to learn more about the exact techniques needed to strike the many types of shots in soccer or if you are interested in step-by-step instructions on how to score by using most of the ways described in the previous chapter's chart, then grab the *Understand Soccer* series book, *Soccer Shooting & Finishing,* to increase the power of your shot by up to 100% and become more accurate. These will allow you to feel great after games, knowing the team relied on you to win.

Chapter 11

Warm Up Your Mind

It is important for a soccer player to warm up their body before a game. However, most soccer players forget that they should also warm up their minds. You can have a fully warmed-up body, but if your mind is not prepared to play, then you will find your performance lacking. **Therefore, consider the following keys to a great pre-game mind warm-up:**

1. Have a Routine
2. Focus on Process Behaviors
3. Mentally Rehearse

Key #1: Have a Routine

Having a pre-game routine ensures that you have a consistent plan to help you before a game and to increase your internal locus of control. Pre-game routines consist of drills and dynamic stretches that push blood into the muscles and synovial fluids into the joints. To learn how to warm up your body before any game, as all soccer players should, grab a copy of the *Understand Soccer* series book, *Soccer Fitness,* to learn the exact steps needed to increase your performance and avoid injury. Also, your pre-game routine should focus on the mental side of your game too. A routine is like a funnel that channels your focus to ensure you are ready to play soccer. Pre-game routines help you remain focused on the important items while avoiding mental distractions. **For example, you can have a few phrases to tell yourself before every game, such as:**

-I am calm, cool, and collected.

-I am a goal-scorer.

-I am a hard worker.

-I am prepared for this moment.

-I am focused.

-I am unstoppable.

-I am relentless.

-I am unshakable.

-I am a leader.

-I am a winner.

Key #2: Focus on Process Behaviors

Next, remember that soccer is a team sport with 22 players in total and referees who also help to decide the outcome of the game. Therefore, be focused on what you can control. **"Process behaviors" represent what a soccer player has control over and can perform regardless of how the game is unfolding. Things like being aggressive, playing** hard, **staying level-headed, keeping your head up, having fun, communicating, and being positive with yourself and teammates are examples of "process behaviors."** A soccer player can stay committed to these attitudes throughout a game, whether or not it is going well. Focus on the process and you will increase the likelihood of positive results happening.

Key #3: Mental Rehearsal

Think about the things you can do in the game to make sure you perform most effectively. Given that I play as a striker for my team, some things I mentally rehearse and visualize before games are:

- ✓ Keeping my head down to keep my form together while shooting;
- ✓ Swiveling my head so that I know where the opposition is when I receive a pass from a defender or midfielder; and
- ✓ Using the self-pass when a defender reaches in for the ball.

Mental Routine + Physical Routine = Success

In conclusion, soccer is as much a mental game as it is a physical one. Focus on both your mental and your physical routines prior to game time to ensure your mind and body are ready to go. Understand that process behaviors are things you can always control because they help describe your mindset. **Additionally, mentally rehearse the items which you know will make the biggest impact on your game.** These rehearsals are position-specific and should differ for each player. Finally, remember that you can also have a morning routine upon waking to start off your day right and ensure your eventual success.

YouTube: If you would like to learn how to warm up your mind before a game in a video format, then watch the *Understand Soccer* YouTube video: *Soccer Warm Up - How to Get Your Mind Ready*.

Chapter 12

Mentally Tough

In the chapter on locus of control, it explained that you must take responsibility for everything you can control. **However, there are certain things outside your control that you just must accept and move on, such as the weather, the field you play on, and the officiating.** According to a former United States Marine, Michael Eldridge, "It is mind over matter; if you do not mind, then it does not matter." Therefore, as a soccer player, you must strive to be mentally tough.

At Next Level Training, the premier soccer training program in Michigan, there is a saying in large letters on the wall that says, "It is 75°F and sunny." Many soccer players make the excuse that it was raining, windy, too hot, too cold, muddy, etc. My soccer mentor, Aaron Byrd, jokingly says to players making weather excuses that even though it was raining for your team, it was 75°F and sunny for the other team. He is poking fun at the trainee's attitude because the opposing team had to play through the same poor conditions as the trainee's team did. **However, because the opposing team did not concern themselves with things they could not control, they were better able to prepare for**

the things they could. They had a tougher mindset to avoid having the weather and field conditions as excuses for why things were not going their way. Remember, winners WIN! Having bad weather or poor field conditions as an excuse reveals a weak mindset. However, a team should understand the pros and cons of each condition to help their team's game plan. See the chart below:

Different Field Types			
	Attacking	**Defending**	**Goalkeeping**
Dry Turf Field	Helps	Hurts	Even
Wet Grass or Turf Field	Hurts	Helps	Hurts
Indoor Field	Helps	Hurts	Even
Short Grass Field	Helps	Hurts	Even
Long Grass Field	Hurts	Helps	Helps
Boarded Field	Helps	Hurts	Hurts
Muddy Field	Hurts	Helps	Helps
Uneven/Clumpy Field	Hurts	Helps	Hurts

Even if you disagree with one or two of the above examples, you still must understand that poorer field conditions generally help defenders because passing and foot skills become more difficult to use. The better the field conditions, the easier it is for attackers to score and use their strengths. For goalkeepers, conditions around the net are their only concerns. **Use these conditions to your advantage when possible.** Make sure you increase the number of shots you take when playing in the rain or on a wet field because the goalie will have a much tougher time judging and handling the ball. It is best to know that being a defender on a muddy, uneven, clumpy, or long-grass field will make it easier for the other team's attackers to make mistakes and thus for you to stop them. Understand that being an attacking player on a perfectly trimmed grass or turf field will make it much easier to dribble and pass.

A great way to reframe unfavorable situations that are out of your control is to find the silver lining. First, finding the silver lining teaches your mind to look for the good in every situation and to be more grateful, which is so important. Second, you can benefit from the silver lining. Try it! **Say aloud, "[insert the thing you dislike here] benefits me because [insert the silver lining here]."**

For example, say you are a defender and are playing in a game when it is 100°F outside. You can complain all you want, but it will not change the temperature of the game. To find the silver lining, you might say, "It is 100°F outside, and that benefits me because forwards and strikers on the other team must play in this heat, too, and all their explosive cuts and runs will be more tiring than usual. The heat gives me an advantage in the game." Being able to reframe situations that seem bad into situations that are good will help you become a mentally tough soccer player.

Chapter 13

Do Not Worry About a Bad Call

In soccer, as in most other sports, referees ensure fairness for both teams. Sometimes, the referee may make decisions and award calls that you believe are unfair and undeserved. However, by constantly blaming the referee and implying that their actions are the only reason for your loss, you are telling your subconscious mind to blame others for the poor outcomes in your life. Surely, referees make terrible calls sometimes, and I am not suggesting that there are never times when they make mistakes. **However, 99 times out of 100, once a referee makes a call, they will stay firm in their decision.**

As a player complaining, you are wasting your time, sapping your energy, and reducing your emotional capital on something that cannot be changed. **Even worse, this bad call is distracting you from the rest of the game and the steps needed to overcome the referee's bad call.** Make sure you are focusing on the things that can be changed. Even if the referee made a terrible decision at the end of a game that cost your team a goal and ultimately the victory, remind yourself there were 89 other minutes of soccer played where you had many other opportunities to score to ensure that it was not in the referees' hands to change the outcome of the game. Let me restate that a good soccer team will aim to win by a few goals, so even if the ref makes a terrible call or two, your team still has room for error on the referees' part.

The reverse of being a calm player who respects the referee is yelling at the referee any time they make a mistake. Having refereed games myself, I know I am less likely to make a call in favor of that team if they are constantly hassling me and judging every single decision I make. Therefore, make sure the coach has selected a captain or someone on the team who is designated to talk to the referee. Should the referee make a mistake, the coach can have the designated person calmly explain that they disagree with the referee's call, explain why quickly, and then move on mentally from there. **Even if that player provides valid arguments, the referee likely will not change their decision but may look to make up for that decision later in a game or at least make sure not to make a similar error again.** Soccer players find it embarrassing when their teammates yell at the officials or lose their composure because it hardly ever helps the team. Worst of all, your teammates may look down on you for often complaining and being easily distracted by the referee's actions.

In conclusion, harassing a referee generally only make things worse. If you want to be a great soccer player, you will need to lead by example. By pointing out the referee's flawed calls, you are reinforcing the idea that others need to change for you to receive what you want. Also, yelling at the referee will make the referee less likely to make a call in favor of your team later in the game. Although referees can make mistakes (and often do), remember that they are just humans trying to do their best, just like you. Give them a break or two, show them respect, and focus on the areas of soccer you can control.

YouTube: If you would like to learn how to not worry about a bad call by watching a video, then watch the *Understand Soccer* YouTube video: *How to Not Worry About a Bad Call*.

Chapter 14

Cristiano Ronaldo's Mindset

What good would a soccer book on mindset be without discussing the mindset of one of the greatest soccer players ever to play the game? From his goal-scoring prowess to his huge cabinet of trophies, Cristiano Ronaldo (also known as "CR7", due to his uniform number) is an outstanding performer whom the world is lucky to have witnessed play.

His unique outlook in soccer is defined as follows:

-He is a continual learner;

-He has confidence in his actions—even if he comes across setbacks;

-He works harder than his competitors; and

-He has the desire to win.

He is a Continual Learner

Cristiano Ronaldo has said, *"I feel an endless need to learn, to improve, to evolve, not only to please the coach and the fans but also feel satisfied with myself."* This quote of Ronaldo highlights that he realizes continually learning is the best way to get ahead and necessary to stay ahead. Since he was a young soccer player, he has been focused on daily improvement. To reach his ever-larger goals, he must take the deliberate steps to achieve his short-term goals that ultimately add up to creating his long-term successes at the pinnacle of soccer. Most players work hard to travel to the top. Ronaldo worked incredibly hard to be there and continues to put in the work to stay there. At Cristiano Ronaldo's level, he realizes that developing his skills both on and off the field is necessary to grow continually as a soccer player.

He Has Confidence Despite Setbacks

Cristiano Ronaldo understands that confidence is a learnable skill, and it can be developed with practice. He has even said, *"In my mind, I'm always the best. I do not care what people think, what they say. In my mind, not just this year but always, I'm always the best."* These are powerful statements that some may view as skewed, boastful, or even harmful. However, Ronaldo understands that he needs to have confidence in what he does—even if other people think he is too over the top with his remarks and beliefs.

Ronaldo viewed himself as the best long before he ever was considered one of the best. There can be little doubt that his self-belief has helped make him a top performer. Because Ronaldo truly believes that he is meant to be the best, he trains hard to become more knowledgeable than his competition. There are countless setbacks we can point to on the field but often it is the off-the-field problems that are the most difficult challenges. At 15 years-old, Ronaldo was diagnosed with a racing heart according to his mother, Dolores Aveiro—something most athletes could not overcome. He decided soccer was too important and had the operation to fix the problem so he could come back to the game he loves. This example reveals that he does not let setbacks stop him, even though they may slow him down in the short-term.

He Works Harder Than His Competitors

Though some natural talent has made it possible for him to be decent at soccer, he became great because of his work ethic. After all, it is easy to find players who have talent who never become the player who so many parents and coaches expected them to become. **Cristiano Ronaldo has a first to arrive and last to leave training mentality with practice to ensure no one is receiving more from training than him.** In fact, he trains 3 to 4 hours per day to remain at peak physical state and to ensure that his skills are game ready.

Let us look at how he works hard to prepare for a game and the ways he ensures quick recovery after a game. **The night before a game, Ronaldo is a huge advocate of obtaining enough sleep.** He knows that great sleep is critical to recover from training and to be rested for the training the following day. Do you want to learn more about how to obtain a great night sleep every night and feel well-rested in the morning to have the energy to tackle all the tasks you usually feel to sluggish to do? Then, pick up a copy of the *Understand Soccer* series book, *Soccer Sleep*, for the step-by-step guide to obtain terrific sleep every night, so you will feel well-rested in the morning and happy to take on the day. In fact, Ronaldo aims for at least eight hours of sleep a night.

Upon waking, Ronaldo likes to do a short workout in the morning to ensure he can fit in exercise wherever he can. In an interview with *Goal.com*, Ronaldo revealed that he even performs abdominal workouts to start his day and before going to bed. According to Ronaldo, *"If you get into a routine, then it makes it easier. It will become a habit."* Similarly, nutrition is no light matter to Ronaldo. He prefers up to six small meals each day because *"a good workout must be combined with a good diet."* Like Lionel Messi, Ronaldo eats meals high in protein, with whole grains, fruit, and vegetables.

Before a match, Ronaldo has pre-game habits. He starts his warm-up even before his teammates start. Part of this involves looking at his own reflection to psych himself up mentally for the game. **Like Alex Morgan, Ronaldo understands the importance of staying as relaxed as possible.** His thoughts will be on what will happen in the game while moving, stretching, listening to music, and having fun to lighten the serious mood of playing in soccer matches with millions of eyes watching him.

After the game is completed and often won, he has post-game habits that help ensure his health and long-term success. Ronaldo goes so far to say, **"Recovery is more important to me than actual training sessions."** Well, when you play at least 50 games a year, it is understandable why Ronaldo takes his recovery so seriously. From drinking water and consuming food to refuel his body to varying between hot and cold baths, he goes to great lengths to promote the recovery of his body. He even goes for post-game swims. Remember, most soccer player will stretch for a few minutes and likely grab some food as their only post-game habits. All of Ronaldo's productive habits led Juventus' medical staff to say that he has the physical capacity of a 20-year-old when he joined the club at age 33.

He Has the Desire to Win

Former Manchester United teammate Quinton Fortune leaves us with this final thought on Cristiano Ronaldo's mindset: *"He had the desire to win, and his talent was unbelievable. You get a lot of talented players who don't have the desire to do the work, but Ronaldo puts in the work. His desire got him to where he is today. I've never seen anything like it because every single day he came into training, he was doing extra: shooting, dribbling, scissors, going to the gym, wanting to be stronger, and quicker to be better every single day."* Interested in learning about all the potential positions in soccer, including CR7's position as a winger? Then, grab the *Understand Soccer* series book, *Soccer Positions*.

YouTube: If you would like to learn about Cristiano Ronaldo's Mindset in a video format, then watch the *Understand Soccer* YouTube video: *Cristiano Ronaldo's Mindset*.

Chapter 15

Visualization

Renato Susnja, former Division 1 college midfielder and now an outstanding soccer trainer at Next Level Training in the metropolitan Detroit area often says that it is important to **"anticipate, do not react."** This attitude allows you to imagine what will happen *before* it happens. Expecting a play to happen, which is a type of in-game visualization, affords you the time needed to make an action plan.

Visualization before you take a shot is nearly as effective as actually having taken a practice shot according to the famous Australian psychologist, Alan Richardson, who conducted a sports experiment proving visualization's worth for athletes. This is huge because you know how you are always better going through a drill the second time than you are the first time in practice? Well, having your first lap in your mind will make the second lap way better, which is really only the first lap in reality. Grab a copy of the *Understand Soccer* series book, *Soccer Passing & Receiving*, to learn more about how to make a plan and how it will increase the number of goals and assists you will earn in a season.

Let us look at Alex Morgan, the forward on the Women's United States National Team, who is an Olympic gold medalist and World Cup Champion. Alex Morgan has stated, "I never get too hyped up too early before a game — I feel like that leads to having restless legs and mind." Alex Morgan says she prefers to **"Do a lot of mental visualization and use breathing techniques to calm myself down before a game."** Therefore, she likes to use pre-game visualization to ensure she can go over likely situations in the game, even before the game starts. This allows her to determine what she would do to score, provide an assist for a teammate, take a penalty kick, or act in a particular situation.

It is as easy as sitting in a chair, on the field, or even in the car for five to ten minutes before a game while breathing deliberately. Harvard Medical School says to take deep breaths. The air coming in through your nose should move downward into your lower belly and let your abdomen expand fully. Avoid breathing where your chest is going up and down as this can lead you to being more anxious. Now, breathe out through your mouth or your nose, if that feels more natural. **Avoid shallow breathing because it feels tense and constricted, while deep breathing produces relaxation.** Next, visualize the likely scenarios you will encounter in a game. Scenarios have been broken down by position:

Forwards:

-Perfectly placing a penalty kick;

-Easily using a body feint (i.e., jab step) in a 1v1 against a defender;

-Shooting on net while keeping your head down; and

-The great feeling of scoring or earning an assist.

Midfielders:

-Making the perfect pass to a forward who scores;

-Using the self-pass to beat players on the opposing team who are reaching in for the ball;

-Working past the point where your body is tired and wants to slow down; and

-Scoring from outside the 18-yard box with a powerful shot.

Defenders:

-Blocking the opposing team's shots while keeping your hands behind your body;

-Flawlessly executing the stepover when you have the ball and your back is facing the net you need to score in;

-Stopping an opposing forward who is attempting to dribble past you; and

-Clearing the ball to the perfect spot for your forwards to take possession.

Goalkeepers:

-Reacting correctly to stop an opponent's penalty kick;

-Throwing/kicking the ball accurately up the field to a teammate;

-Working hard to save the other team's shots; and

-Yelling directions to your defenders when you want them to adjust their positioning.

In conclusion, using visualization will help you achieve the 10,000 hours of deliberate practice to achieve mastery in soccer. Also, visualization will make the game easier because you have already experienced it once before in your own mind. Just 5-10 minutes of visualization can produce huge results for you and your team. Thankfully, you do not need to be perfect to start; you can begin by using the guidelines above, and in time, you may find even better ways to visualize your own success.

YouTube: If you would like to learn how to get better at soccer without even touching a ball, then watch the *Understand Soccer* YouTube video: *Playing Soccer Using Visualization*.

Chapter 16

Future Truths

Like pre-game and in-game visualization, you can use future truths to help yourself advance quickly up the soccer rankings. **Specifically, future truths are a way of training your mind to become comfortable with something you want to happen in the future.** Yes, this technically is a current lie. But are you willing to lie to yourself today (in a very positive way) to produce the future you truly desire?

Personally, I am willing to do that! Here is a shortened version of the future truths I told myself long before they ever came true:

-I have an outgoing personality;
-I am at peace;
-I am funny;
-I am a #1 best-selling soccer author;
-I have thick skin;
-I am a great storyteller;
-I am secure;
-I am a source of inspiration;
-I take feedback well; and
-I am fulfilled.

If you keep telling yourself a future truth, then you will associate that truth with the person you want to become. More importantly, you will figure out the actions you need to take to make those future truths become a reality. For example, let us say you are a girl who wants to be a forward for the United States Women's National Team. One of the easiest things to do to achieve this goal is to tell yourself you will be a forward on the United States Women's National Team. Say it out loud! "I will be a forward on the United States Women's National Team." Say it out loud one more time! Now, let me ask you two questions:

1. Was the future truth you stated uncomfortable to say?
2. Did you feel like you were lying to yourself?

Remember, it is a current lie, but it is not a future lie. It is a future truth. **Are you willing to lie to yourself in the current moment to become the best player in your league or would you rather be true to your current self and probably not even be the best player on your team?** That is a decision for you to make but the more you say future truths, the more you will believe them. If you say a statement like, "I am an average soccer player," it is a self-fulfilling prophecy, so you will not take the time and energy to learn how to be the best player in your league. However, if you say future truths repeatedly and take the action required to achieve it, you will make the future truths come true. Have future truths that will make it easier for you to make decisions like, "Should I go watch television this afternoon or would working on my shot with my opposite foot for 30 minutes be more helpful for me to become a forward on the United States Women's National Team?"

You do not need to know every step you should take from this point until you achieve your future truth. You just need to start, work hard, never give up, and understand you will better see the next steps needed as you begin down the path towards your future truth. Even if you do not have your driver's license yet, just imagine you want to drive somewhere. Would you wait to leave until all the lights are green or would you just drive and understand that you will have some red lights on your journey you must overcome but will have a clearer view of the path as you travel down it? Here are some future truths you can implement into your mindset today, sorted by position:

Everyone:
-I am continually learning;
-I am a leader;
-I communicate well;
-I am not afraid to make mistakes; and
-I am open to feedback.

Forwards:
-I score easily;
-I am fast;
-My foot skills allow me to take many shots;
-My shots are accurate; and
-I have powerful headers.

Midfielders:

-I create opportunities for my teammates to score;
-I am calm in the middle of the field;
-I am a playmaker;
-I am great at shooting outside of the 18-yard box; and
-I have amazing endurance.

Defenders:

-I am a terrific shot-blocker;
-I am physical;
-I easily steal the ball from the other team;
-I am great at winning the ball in the air; and
-I am dominant in 1v1s.

Goalkeepers:

-I tell my defenders what to do;
-I make tons of saves;
-I have a short memory of goals I let in;
-I start my team's counterattacks with accurate throws and kicks; and
-I am tough.

Coaches:

-My players love playing for me;
-I provide feedback in ways that my players are receptive;
-I learn from my mistakes;
-I am a winner; and
-I enjoy working with parents.

The above list of future truths is not all-encompassing, but it provides a good starting point for a soccer player based on their position, as well as the first list of future truths that applies to everyone. Even though this book is specifically for soccer players, you can use the concept of future truths in every area of your life. Use it for your schoolwork, friends, family, spiritual beliefs, etc. Do not forget to add your personalized current truths, as well. **Act like the person you want to be in order to become them.** As the wise philosopher Socrates once said, *"Be as you wish to seem."*

If you are interested in a more complete list of "I am" statements and future truths that you can use to build your confidence and mindset, then make sure to get the free "Morning Habit Checklist" at UnderstandSoccer.com/free-printout.

Chapter 17

It is Okay to Make Mistakes

Steve Corder, a former Division 1 college coach and soccer player at the University of Detroit Mercy, once said something to a group he was training that left a lasting impression upon me. Steve stated, ***"In soccer and in life, you will make hundreds of thousands of mistakes over your lifetime. Once the mistake occurs, it no longer matters that you made the mistake; it only matters how you react to the mistake."***

Most people see mistakes and failures as the same thing. **However, failures are mistakes that have been left uncorrected.** If you make a mistake, learn from it, and then correct your actions—this is how you can quickly succeed. Life's greatest lessons are usually learned at the worst times and from the greatest mistakes. In the quote in the previous paragraph, Steve teaches that you cannot get caught up in your past actions. Instead, you must do whatever you can in the present to place yourself in the best situation to succeed in the future. Therefore, if you just made a mistake, the best thing you can do is to take responsibility for it, figure out what happened, learn from it, and then move on.

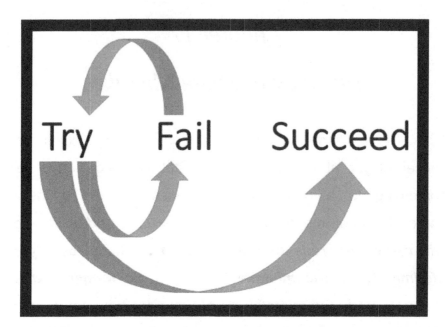

Try Fail Succeed

When recovering from a mistake, do not make the mistake worse by worrying about it. Recover from it as quickly as you can to avoid wasting time in the present that can be better used for the future. Personally, I suffered for years from the fear of not being perfect. This caused me not to do many things because I was worried about what others would think. Even worse, I was crippled with fear because of my laser-like focus on the mistakes I made. When I did something, I had to check it three times. Then, after reading several books to improve my view of mistakes, I swung too far in the other direction to where I was not concerned *enough* about errors, to the point at which I was not even checking my work at all. This was bad because I mentally became okay with making mistakes, but I was not taking the steps necessary to *learn* from them.

When working on something, check your work once. Any more than that and you are likely just wasting time—unless you are performing something very serious and it is the difference between life or death. Not checking your work at all will create sloppy/lazy mistakes. Again, mistakes are great learning tools, but there is a fine line between doing your best in a reasonable period of time but still making a mistake as opposed to being lazy/sloppy and making *careless* mistakes.

For example, perhaps your coach is demonstrating a dribbling and foot skills drill that your team will be practicing. Perfectionists would have anxiety about going through the drill because they might make mistakes. Perfectionists would want to be the last one in the line to see others perform the drill before starting and so hopefully no one will see if they make a mistake. On the other hand, sloppy players will go through the drill and make mistakes at seemingly every cone because they did not pay attention as the coach was giving directions. **It is ideal to be the person in the front of the line who is helping the coach demonstrate the drill, is actively watching and listening to the coach's directions on what to do at each set of cones, and understands he or she may make a mistake or two on their first lap or when helping to show how to perform the drill.** However, this same person will have done a good portion of the drill correctly and will have learned from his or her mistakes when going through the drill the second time. If you are looking for drills with specific coaching points to use in practices in order to increase your player's skills, grab the *Understand Soccer* series book, *Soccer Drills*.

In conclusion, avoid lazy mistakes, but do not be so worried that you must be perfect in everything you do. After all, **perfectionism is an excuse for procrastination.** Oppositely, Albert Einstein was right when he said, *"Anyone who has never made a mistake has never tried anything new."*

YouTube: If you would like to see a video on why it is okay to make mistakes, then watch the *Understand Soccer* YouTube video: *Are Mistakes Bad or Good for You?*

Chapter 18

Reducing the 10,000-Hour Rule

When learning anything in life, there is a learning curve involved. **A learning curve describes how much time is needed to become better at something.** In this chapter, we will further explain its impact and how to reduce your learning curve. K. Anders Ericsson, the author of the book, *Peak*, points out that to become an expert in the field of your choosing, it takes about 10,000 hours of deliberate practice. Some fields require less, and others require more, but 10,000 hours is an easy number to remember. Your learning curve dictates your journey to the 10,000-hour mark.

Everyone's learning curve is slightly different, as is the learning curve for each skill you want to learn. Though not every player can become Lionel Messi or Cristiano Ronaldo, they can still become world-class with enough deliberate practice, learning, and hard work. Playing soccer well involves an increasing return learning curve, as shown in the following image:

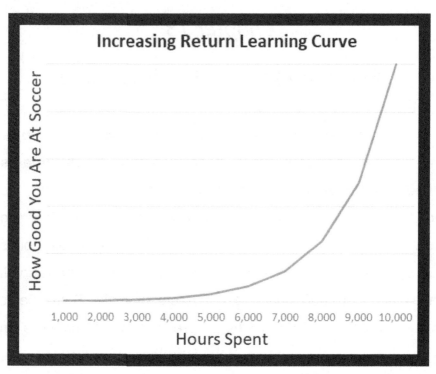

Increasing Return Learning Curve

How Good You Are At Soccer (vertical axis)

1,000 2,000 3,000 4,000 5,000 6,000 7,000 8,000 9,000 10,000

Hours Spent

A soccer player can add skills and abilities quicker when they have a solid foundation. For a soccer player just starting out, there is a ton to learn, and their feet are not as coordinated yet. Often, soccer players start at a young age, so their minds cannot grasp things as quickly yet, and they do not have much strength in their undeveloped bodies. **However, as a soccer player matures both mentally and physically, it becomes much easier to understand how to learn skills and when to use those skills in games, such as when to pass and how to receive passes with the correct form, how to strike a soccer ball five different ways, how to understand in-depth game planning to take advantage of an opposing team's tactics, etc.** Therefore, the increasing return learning curve means that a soccer player is acquiring skills, speed, and strength at an ever-increasing rate, until the maximum learning potential is reached. Soccer falls under this category because of the complexity of the sport, and all the variables that can be learned.

On the other hand, the diminishing return learning curve shows a higher increase in skill at the beginning. However, it decreases with time, until it reaches zero additional skill for each additional hour spent. At this point, the person has achieved the maximum skill level. **The diminishing return learning curve indicates that, initially, there are huge gains in learning with little time invested.** This typically occurs with skills that are less complex.

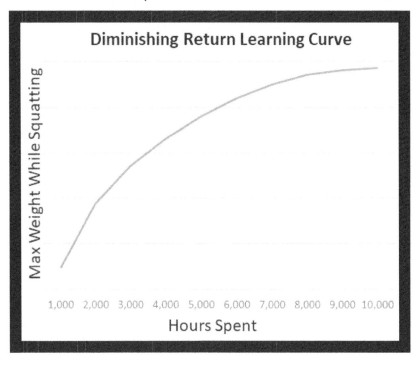

Consider the example of the diminishing return learning curve in the previous image. For a person attempting to increase their weight for a barbell back squat, they realize huge increases in strength very early. However, as the person's knowledge on form, nutrition, and training increases, the additional weight a person can add is very small with each new workout.

Weightlifters find it easy to work towards squatting 250 lbs. It takes planning and a lot of time to increase their squat to 500 lbs. Most weightlifters will spend their whole careers working to have a 750 lb. squat, and the few individuals with favorable genetics, large femurs, and big body frames will find they generally max out at around 1,000 lbs. The reduction in pounds is a terrific example of diminishing returns for less complex tasks.

At this point, you are likely comfortable with how learning curves work but may be thinking, "Wow, 10,000 hours is a lot to spend playing soccer to become better at it!" I definitely agree. 10,000 hours of deliberate practice is no small feat and going down the path of becoming a great soccer player takes time and dedication. **However, there are a few loopholes that will allow you to attain 10,000 hours in significantly less time.** Because there are many ways to reduce the 10,000-hour rule, let us apply the logic we learned in the chapter on the 80/20

Principle to figure out which ones will provide us the largest impact with the least amount of work.

The loophole that will provide you with 80% of the results in 20% of the time is finding a mentor. A mentor does not need to be Lionel Messi or Cristiano Ronaldo, as these individuals likely would not have the time and would be very expensive. Furthermore, they are so incredibly skilled that most soccer players working with these two superstars would give up before realizing their full potential because in their minds they would not believe they could ever be like Lionel Messi or Cristiano Ronaldo.

It is best to start with a mentor who is a few years ahead of you and can teach you the things you need to become better at performing to quickly become a much more effective soccer player. As you grow, you can add different mentors who have new and/or advanced skills. An in-person mentor would be the most ideal, but because this can cost a significant of money and tons of time, most people find that mentoring through books and online videos is better for them.

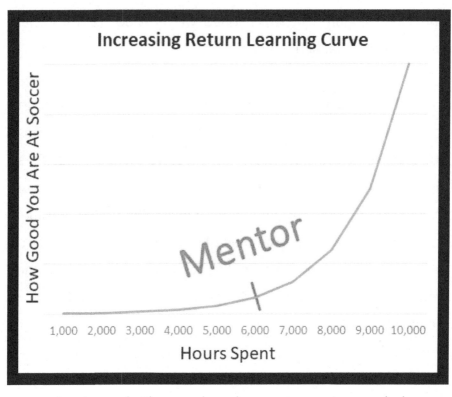

Increasing Return Learning Curve

How Good You Are At Soccer (y-axis)

Mentor

1,000 2,000 3,000 4,000 5,000 6,000 7,000 8,000 9,000 10,000

Hours Spent

As shown in the previous image, a mentor can help you jump the learning curve. **By finding and learning from a mentor, you can invest the time they have spent playing, learning, and making mistakes into your own skills and abilities so that it may take you only 4,000 hours of deliberate practice guided by a mentor to reach the same point as a soccer player who spent 10,000 hours without a mentor.** There is a Russian expression stating, *"A dumb person makes the same mistake over and over again. A smart person learns from their mistakes. A wise person learns from someone else's mistakes."* Therefore, I challenge you to be the wise person who learns from other people's mistakes.

A mentor can give you a guide and/or model to follow that will help you figure out the path quicker than if you attempted to figure it yourself. A $10 "how-to book" on soccer, or a $47 video course on soccer, are both very cheap when you consider that you will be taking someone else's years of successes, failures, studies, and experiences and investing it into your game after just a few hours spent on a book, video, or course. This concept is life changing. Do not be a soccer player who slowly gets better; find a mentor who will allow you to jump the 10,000-hour learning curve.

Other loopholes to consider are learning how to become better from your coach(es) or parent(s). A coach can be a mentor, but more often than not, their focus is on many players on the team and not just your specific skills and abilities. **Coaches often focus on getting the team to work better and not necessarily on getting each individual player to become better themselves.**

Also, you can learn from a teammate who gives you advice after making a mistake. Most people are offended when others give them feedback and I will be honest and say I was like this for many years. However, it has been said, **"If you correct a fool, he will hate you; correct a wise man and he will love you."** I speak from experience when I say I was once a fool to feedback, but it is way more rewarding to be wise to feedback. As such, be the wise soccer player open to feedback from teammates, coaches, and parents.

Additionally, you are human and will make mistakes. **Therefore, it is a must that you are okay with making a mistake once but figuring out why you made it and how to correct it going forward.** Furthermore, you can watch other soccer players to learn from their success and mistakes. Watching the English Premier League, La Liga, Bundesliga, Serie A, Ligue 1, MLS, and even your own footage will help you see how the best players perform and where your game can be improved. Lastly, visualizing your skills and practicing them in your mind is nearly as effective as performing them on the field, so you can almost always find time to visualize even if you do not have time to make it to the soccer field to train.

In conclusion, the soccer learning curve can be steep. Find a mentor to help you on your journey to become a great soccer player. **A mentor is a great way to help you achieve your 10,000 hours in less time, so you can experience the success you have dreamed about.** Do not be a player who avoids this advice and watches their teammates and opponents become better than you.

Afterword

I hope you have learned how to open your mind to feedback from others, become okay with making mistakes, and view the game as a springboard to achieve your goals. Your attitude towards both soccer and the world will make a huge impact on your success. Having a positive attitude does not make a situation any easier. However, it does make the situation seem easier. Therefore, I challenge you to continue growing your knowledge of the game. Find at least one mentor to help you leap over your competition knowing that you do not need to make the mistakes yourself because you can learn from somebody else's mistakes.

Avoid the pain of missing out on the technology age we currently live in where access to resources and information on how to improve your soccer game is easily available and very affordable. Remember that changing/growing can be scary at times. However, it is much scarier to stay the same when everyone around you is becoming better. As a result, know that you are trading discomfort in the current moment for future success. If it seems like you are going through tough times, do not stop. Overcome the tough times so you can have the success you so badly desire on the other side. As the United States Women's Soccer Team's all-star forward, Alex Morgan, points out, "You are your biggest competition."

Soccer Sleep:

A Step-by-Step Guide on How to Get a Good Night's Sleep Every Single Night

Introduction

First, I am not a medical doctor. I am simply a person who went from being a terrible sleeper who could not fall asleep because my mind would race. I would wake up often in the middle of the night and lay there, wide-eyed, for hours. I would especially feel tired and mentally hazy during the day.

By learning the different mindsets and sleeping tricks explained in this book, it has allowed me to become a much better sleeper. Now, I can fall asleep within five minutes, sleep soundly throughout the night, and wake up feeling energized and well-rested—even on those days when I only achieved a few hours of sleep. This book will show you how to feel great by becoming a terrific sleeper, too. Starting in Chapter Four, I will cover much of the research and science behind sleep.

To make this book easy to read, I have broken it into the following sections: (1) Mindset; (2) Daytime; (3) Nighttime; (4) Sleep Time; and (5) The Next Morning.

Section 1 – Mindset

Chapter 1

Have Less Rules

Most people do not realize it, but they have their own set of rules for what is a good night's sleep. For example, some people believe that they must sleep for eight straight hours without waking, not have any dreams, not wake up before 9 a.m., and must feel 100% refreshed upon waking to have a restful night's sleep. If any of these self-created "rules" are not met, then they have a great excuse for why they are tired, groggy, or lethargic the next day. As you can imagine, the person who needs to meet all these self-imposed "rules" will likely have a tough time obtaining a good night's sleep.

Therefore, make your "rules" for a good night's sleep easier to achieve. For example, my current rule for obtaining a good night's sleep is "I need to wake up in the morning."

That is it!

Please understand that I used to be a terrible sleeper because I had a poor set of rules, which left me feeling mentally foggy the next day. This happened at least 5-6 days per week.

Some of my rules included:

1. I had to have at least eight hours of sleep each night.
2. I could not wake up a single time in the middle of the night.
3. I had to feel 100% refreshed and rejuvenated upon waking.

These may sound familiar because these are the same lousy criteria of the person in the opening paragraph of this chapter! The simpler you can make your "rules," the easier it is for you to achieve a good night's sleep. Now, it is no way implied that one hour of sleep is the equivalent of a full eight hours of sleep. However, sleeping well for most is tough enough as it is, so do not have rules that make it harder than it needs to be. If you have things that are working well for your sleep, focus on being grateful for those.

Do you have a bed to sleep in? Do you live in a community where you are not scared to go to bed because you do not fear anything happening to you in your sleep? Do you have a pillow and a blanket? Did you have time to get any nighttime rest? Answering simple questions like these to help uncover things you are grateful to have when sleeping will make it much easier to focus on all the good you have going for your ability to sleep rather than focusing on how often you wake in the middle of the night or sometimes have a hard time turning off your mind when going to bed.

Because I made my rules easier to achieve, I made obtaining a good night's sleep much more successful. I suggest you look at your current rules for a good night's sleep and see if you can make it easier for yourself to win. **A study entitled "Placebo Sleep Affects Cognitive Functioning" was recently published in the *Journal of Experimental Psychology*. It revealed that just *believing* that you had a good night's sleep provides similar benefits to *actually* having a good night's sleep.** This study showed that if you believe you are well-rested, your brain will perform significantly better the next day, regardless of the actual quality of your sleep.

The opposite holds true, too. Constantly talking about how tired you are—which is normal in our culture—has been shown to be detrimental to your mental and physical performance. Therefore, to an extent, the quality of your sleep is in your mind. For me, I can get up go to the bathroom in the middle of the night, I can be woken up by my wife, I can obtain less than the full seven to eight hours of sleep I aim to achieve, or countless other things can happen. However, none of those are that bad and therefore I can still achieve what I have decided for myself is a good night's sleep.

In the remaining chapters of this book, there are numerous ways to increase the likelihood of achieving a great night's sleep. A great way to start is by making your rules for a good night's sleep easier to achieve. Also, stop telling yourself and others how tired you are today! Your future self will thank you.

Chapter 2

Future Truths for Better Sleep

One of the biggest problems with people who are not good sleepers is they constantly tell themselves they are not good sleepers. There are certainly people who are worse sleepers than others and have medical conditions to prove it, but there is a big difference between having those problems and using those problems to define yourself. The former is out of your control, but the latter is detrimental. If you are constantly telling yourself that you are a bad sleeper, then you, your subconscious mind, and your body will believe this. You will always find several reasons why you are not a good sleeper, and you will likely not take action to become a good sleeper.

Even if you are not a great sleeper currently, tell yourself a future truth. For most people, myself included, telling a lie is not believable and sometimes feels unethical. Therefore, I use future truths instead. These are statements that are not currently true but will become true in the future through your beliefs and actions in the present. **Modern psychology has discovered that whatever statement you attach to the words "I am" almost always become true in your life, if you believe it.** This is both a good and bad thing. It can be bad if you use statements like, "I am bad at math," "I am bad with money," "I am boring," "I am sad," "I am bad at soccer," "I am not good at scoring," and "I am a bad sleeper." Once you attach yourself to those negative views, it is hard to break out of them. Instead, you must realize that you decide what you are and what you are not. Excitingly, these "I am" statements can be great for you, if you instead adopt empowering statements like "I am great at soccer," "I am a great sleeper," "I am caring," "I am friendly," "I am funny," and "I am loved."

With sleep, make sure you are thoughtful about how you use "I am" because you can play a large part in deciding if you "are a good sleeper" or "are a bad sleeper." This concept is also discussed in the *Understand Soccer* series book, *Soccer Parenting*. If you are a parent reading this book, consider ordering a copy of *Soccer Parenting* to learn useful ways to communicate feedback to your soccer player and how to work with and not against the coach of your child's team.

Remember, even if you are not yet a great sleeper, tell yourself a future truth by saying, "I am a great sleeper." By reading this book, you are already taking action towards becoming a better sleeper and improving your performance on the soccer field and in every area of your life. Also, because you are reading this book to gain the skills and knowledge needed to sleep better, you can be comfortable knowing that you are truly telling yourself a future truth.

Section 2 – Daytime

Chapter 3

How to Nap Effectively

Imagine this: You had only six hours of sleep last night; it is the early afternoon and about five hours until game-time. You are tired and want to nap. How should you nap to be the most alert and ready to go for your game?

With napping, each person generally has their preference on how to nap. Sometimes, you wake up feeling refreshed and other times you feel groggier than when you fell asleep. Your preference should also have the facts and studies to support it. According to the National Sleep Foundation, the most important thing to feeling refreshed from a nap is how long you nap. **20 minutes is ideal to obtain the benefits from napping.** The benefits include increased alertness, enhanced soccer performance, and a better mood.

If you are a person who naps for 30-60 minutes, then 10-20 minutes may seem like too little. **However, 10 to 20-minute naps ensure you remain in the lightest stage of sleep. Being in the lightest stage of sleep makes it easier for you to become quickly active again after your nap.** If you make the mistake of napping for 30-60 minutes, you will go into the deeper stages of sleep, and your brainwaves will slow down.

Waking from a deep sleep leaves you mentally groggy. It may not be worth it to take a 30 to 60-minute nap, because you will often feel less alert than you were before you began your nap.

To ensure you just get 10 to 20 minutes, I have found the best thing to do is set an alarm for 22 minutes from the moment you lay down to nap. **Setting an alarm for 22 minutes gives you between 2 and 12 minutes to fall asleep to make sure you stay in the sweet spot of a 10 to 20-minute nap** (how to fall asleep very quickly is discussed in a later chapter). Also, make sure you have your phone/alarm clock far enough away from you. The trick here is to avoid getting up to move your phone away from you. Instead, toss it gently enough out of reach, so you must get up to shut the alarm off.

Having to get up to turn the alarm off will increase your body's blood flow and make it easier to wake up without using the snooze function. **Moving your body increases your blood flow and alertness, so avoid moving prior to taking a nap if you can avoid it.** For example, if you had a long drive in the car and are tired and want to take a nap, stay in the car, have a small pillow handy, and nap. Bringing all your things into the house and then going to your bed to nap will make it much more difficult for you to fall asleep quickly. If you are on the couch, reading or watching television, and you begin to become tired, do not get up and move to your bed to take a nap if you can avoid it. Instead, take your nap on the couch to avoid moving.

Otherwise, the other style of napping that can be ideal for some is a full 90-minute nap. **Specifically, 90 minutes is the time it takes to travel through one sleep cycle. A sleep cycle is where you go from the lightest stage of sleep through the deepest stage of sleep and back to the lightest stage of sleep prior to waking** (a subject discussed more in a later chapter). This style of sleeping will often leave you feeling refreshed and has been shown to boost memory and creativity, but it takes considerably more time.

Lastly, there are better times to take a nap during the day. Assuming that you go to bed at midnight and wake up at 8 a.m., you rarely want to begin a nap after 4 p.m. **Taking a nap too late in the day will make it very hard for you to fall asleep at your usual bedtime, which will often make you more tired the next morning.** Having a nap that makes you more tired the next morning kind of defeats the purpose of napping.

The best time to nap is usually about 1-2 hours after lunch. You will have a dip in your blood-sugar levels at this time, which will make falling asleep very easy. Also, an after-lunch nap is still far enough away from your bedtime that it will not affect your ability to fall asleep at night. If you keep different hours than the 8 a.m.-12 a.m. midnight schedule, then adjust your nap time accordingly. This will ensure great naps that do not prevent you from having a restful night's sleep.

Things to Remember:

-10 to 20-minute naps are best.

-Set your alarm clock for 22 minutes.

-The best time to nap is after lunch.

-Avoid napping within the 8-hour period prior to going to bed.

-Try to limit activity right before falling asleep.

-Place the alarm clock far enough away from you that you must move to shut it off.

Chapter 4

The Importance of Light

Our bodies do a great job of syncing to the time of day and the time of year. During the winter months, when there is less daylight, our bodies are more tired due to a reduction in sunlight. During the summer months, our bodies are more energetic from the increased daylight hours. As a result, technology-related activities can disrupt our body's natural alignment with the time of day and the season.

As night approaches, our bodies release more melatonin. Melatonin is a hormone that our bodies use to help regulate sleep. Our bodies and eyes adjust to the level of brightness to determine how much melatonin to release. This is significant because ensuring your body is properly releasing melatonin will make sleeping much easier and more restful for you. The release of melatonin in the evening and the lack of melatonin in your system during the day is caused by your circadian rhythm. A circadian rhythm coordinates your focus/attitude, metabolism of food, and release of hormones (e.g., melatonin) in your body over the 24-hour day.

Sadly, this natural release of melatonin in the evening can be disrupted by blue/white light from

technology, like televisions, computers, tablets, and cell phones. Blue/white light used to only come from the sun. However, modern advancements in digital screens give off artificial blue/white light that tricks our bodies into releasing less melatonin and making it more difficult for us to fall asleep, stay asleep, and wake up feeling well-rested.

To counteract this, make sure you obtain adequate amounts of exposure to sunlight during the day, so your body can sense when it is lighter outside versus when it is darker outside. Even if you are not directly in the sunlight, being able to see out windows helps to ensure your body is synced up with the time of day. **Additionally, avoid using digital screens within the 30 minutes prior to bedtime.** If you must, there is a setting on your phone and computer to limit the blue/white light given off by the device.

Lastly, there are also blue/white light filtering glasses you can purchase and wear for the hour or so before bedtime to help limit your exposure to blue/white light. This artificial blue/white light prevents deep sleep. **Though you may not enjoy having technology removed from your bedroom, moving the TV or computer from your bedroom at bedtime will make a world of difference in your ability to sleep, too.**

In summary, blue/white light from the sun during the daytime is great because it helps keep you awake and energized. However, artificial blue/white light at night will reduce your body's natural melatonin and make it much harder to fall sleep, stay asleep, and wake up feeling well-rested. Avoid using technology in the 30 minutes before bedtime and if you must, then make sure that the blue/white light reduction setting is turned on for your digital devices, such as your phone, computer, etc.

Chapter 5

Foods You Should Not Consume Late in the Day

For the average person, food before bedtime is not a good idea because the increased need for digestion can cause some restlessness, and the additional calories will probably cause weight gain. However, soccer players are different, and their nutritional needs vary based on their need for higher caloric consumption and/or their goals for their on-field performance. Therefore, consider these three simple rules to determine if and what you should eat before bedtime:

1.Eliminate caffeine
2.Decide whether you want to gain muscle or lose weight
3.Minimize drinks before bed

First, you should know that caffeine supplements and caffeinated beverages can increase performance on the field. However, caffeine is a central nervous system stimulant that gives you energy and mental focus. Energy and mental focus are the last things you want when your head hits the pillow at night! The effects of caffeine kick in 45 minutes after you consume it. **For nearly everyone, the effects of caffeinated beverages like tea, coffee, pre-workout drinks, energy** drinks, or carbonated soda pop last for 4-6 hours. So, avoiding caffeine in the 6 hours prior to bedtime allows you to minimize its impact on your rest. If you are interested in learning more about caffeine, and how it can boost your performance in games, grab a copy of the *Understand Soccer* series book, *Soccer Nutrition*.

Secondly, it is important to set and know your goal for how much you want to weigh and how fit/muscular you are looking to become. As soccer players, we do a ton of running that burns excessive amounts of calories. **Consuming more food and higher quality food will increase your body's ability to gain muscle.** It is highly recommended that you read the *Understand Soccer* series book, *Soccer Fitness*, if you could use more strength, speed, endurance, and/or flexibility as this book will help ensure you become faster and stronger to help your team win more games.

On one hand, if your goal is to gain muscle, then eating before bedtime will provide another opportunity to consume more food and provide the building blocks to gain muscle. **Given that this meal is close to your bedtime, avoid spiking your blood sugar and energy levels by eating foods high in carbohydrates (i.e., sugars). Instead, focus more on foods with healthy fat, fiber, and protein.** Examples of great bedtime foods are vegetables, meats, nuts, seeds, and dairy.

Eating these items will ensure your body takes more time to digest the food, so your muscles are obtaining a steady supply of amino acids (i.e., protein) throughout the night. If you do not eat prior to bedtime, your body will use up whatever nutrition is left in your stomach and then begin to feed off your muscles. Therefore, not eating before bed makes it difficult to build muscle because your body uses your muscles as a source of nutrition during the night.

On the other hand, if your goal is weight loss, then you should limit your pre-bedtime meal, so you are not taking in any excess calories that will limit your body's ability to lose weight. **If you must eat something, it is recommended that you consume slow-digesting casein protein with water or eat cottage cheese to make sure your muscles are fed and to avoid consuming any junk.**

Third, avoid drinking a lot before bed. **You do not want to avoid drinking water altogether because you may become dehydrated in the middle of the night, which can lead to a muscle spasm (i.e., charley horse) in the calves. However, you do not want to consume so much water that you must wake up in the middle of the night to go to the bathroom.** Should this happen to you, there is a chapter in this book on what you should do if you wake up in the middle of the night so that you can fall asleep easier.

According to the Continence Foundation of Australia, an adult bladder can comfortably hold two cups of urine during the day and up to four cups at night. If you are not yet an adult, you can hold less. This means having an 8 oz cup (not a 16 oz glass) of water   before bed should not be problematic—assuming you use the restroom before lying down for the night.

In conclusion, avoid caffeinated beverages six hours prior to bedtime. Eat foods like vegetables, meats, nuts, seeds, and dairy just before you sleep if you are looking to add muscle and are working out. If you are working to lose weight and want to keep your existing muscle mass, then avoid eating before bedtime altogether or consume slow-digesting casein protein with water or eat cottage cheese prior to going to sleep. Lastly, a little water before bedtime is good, but too much will wake you up in the middle of the night.

Section 3 – Nighttime

Chapter 6

Keep a Regular Sleep Schedule

Going to bed at the same time every night can be tough for most people. But honestly, you are not most people. You are taking the time to read and learn more about sleep, and you are willing to do a little more to further your soccer abilities. Obtaining consistent sleep not only impacts your growth in soccer but also makes you happier, more energized, and better able to do well in work, school, etc.

Therefore, having a set bedtime and wake time each weekday and weekend will get your body into a habit that builds you up unlike so many other peoples' bad sleeping habits. For weekends, you may think waking up on the weekend at the same time as the weekday does not sound like much fun. **Then, if you would like to sleep later on the weekends, wake up within 2 hours of the time you would wake up on the weekday.** For example, if you wake up at 7 a.m. during the week, wake up no later than 9 a.m. on the weekend to ensure your body can stay consistent.

The US National Library of Medicine study, "Effects of an Irregular Bedtime Schedule on Sleep Quality, Daytime Sleepiness, and Fatigue," found that participants with an irregular bedtime schedule experienced reduced sleep quality. **Not only does an irregular sleep schedule make it more difficult to fall asleep come Sunday night, but it also reduces the quality of the sleep we are already getting.** These irregular sleep schedules make it harder to achieve the stages of deep sleep (discussed in a later chapter) that our bodies desperately need.

Now, do I have the same perfect sleep schedule day-in and day-out? No, definitely not! However, I do my best to be as consistent as possible. For me, that means that out of the 30 or so days per month, I have a consistent sleeping pattern for about 28 of those days. Life happens, and there are occasionally those nights when you must stay up to complete a big project, or you have the opportunity for a night out with friends that will be a blast and a memory you will not soon forget. However, only being consistent for 15-20 days is not good enough. Staying up too late because you were just scrolling through your social media is not something important nor a good reason to lose precious sleep.

Let me give you a personal example. There was a night when I was a freshman in college, and a bunch of my friends from my dorm asked me if I wanted to go on a bike trip with them around the campus. I was trying to be a good student and be well-rested for class the next day, so I said no to the opportunity for an adventure and a memory. The next day, I woke up well-rested for my class—a class which had no presentation or exam that would have needed 100% of my attention the following day. When I later spoke to my friends, they said they had a blast and explained all the fun stuff they did. Because I was too rigorous and wanted to have a perfect 30 nights each month with a consistent sleep schedule, I missed an opportunity I cannot get back.

In conclusion, being either too rigid or not accountable enough can make it difficult to win at sleeping. **As the leading psychologist Anthony Robbins says,** *"Make your goals winnable."* Therefore, being consistent 28/30 nights per month is definitely achievable and will give you some missed days to make your goal very winnable. Next, if you go to bed late or plan to wake up late, remember the 2-hour rule: **Try not to go to sleep or wake up two hours later than you normally would.** Lastly, if you do not immediately achieve a perfectly consistent bedtime schedule, then give yourself a break. Understand that you are still learning and growing your sleeping skills, and you will work to improve every week.

Chapter 7

The Need for a Bedtime Routine

According to the National Sleep Foundation, a regular nightly routine helps the body recognize that it is bedtime. A bedtime routine could be as simple as reading a book and brushing your teeth, or it could have more steps, such as stretches, affirmations, prayers, journaling, and meditating. It is not too important to concern yourself with how many steps you want your nighttime routine to include. However, making sure you have helpful bedtime habits that are not destructive will make it easier to obtain a restful night's sleep for the rest of your life. Below are some examples of good and bad bedtime routine habits.

Good Bedtime Habits:

-Read a paperback book

-Meditate

-Pray

-Practice personal hygiene, like flossing and brushing your teeth

-Use the restroom

-Journal for what you are grateful

-Write your to-do list for the next day, so it is out of your mind and down on paper

-Listen to peaceful music

-Say your affirmations

-Look at your vision board

-Lightly stretch

-Lay down with 15 minutes to spare

Bad Bedtime Habits:

-Work out immediately before bedtime

-Scroll through social media on your phone

-Be on your computer

-Think about how tired you will be the next morning

-Drink a lot of water

-Listen to metal or rock music

-Watch a scary movie

-Dread the big exam, presentation, or game you have the next day

-Drink a caffeinated beverage, like tea, coffee, or carbonated soda pop

-Start a fight or an emotionally upsetting conversation with a friend or loved one

-Lay down without enough time to fall asleep calmly

Generally, your bedtime routine should start roughly 30 minutes before bedtime. That is a good time to shut off the technology in your house, make sure all the lights are dimmed, and your blue/white light filters are on. Use the 30 minutes prior to bedtime to invest in making yourself better. Do not waste your precious time each evening.

In summary, be mindful of what you do before bedtime. Use those last 30 minutes of the night for a bedtime routine that will help you obtain great sleep. Avoid reserving those 30 minutes for watching a scary television show or scrolling through social media. The great philosopher Aristotle stated, *"We are what we repeatedly do. Excellence, then, is not an act, but a habit."* Therefore, make sure your habits are *building* you and not *breaking* you. Make your sleep schedule easier by repeating your actions every day for an entire month, so they can become habits that are easy to keep and use very little mental energy.

Chapter 8

Review Things You Want to Remember Before Bed

Have you ever thought of the solution to a problem in the shower? Have you ever been working on something, and the answer to something else you have been struggling with pops into your mind instead? This is because when your mind is processing information without actively thinking about it, your subconscious mind is finding the answer. What better way is there to use your subconscious mind to your benefit than to spend your entire night's sleep solving problems and remembering information? If you feed problems and information to your mind before bedtime, you will have another 7-9 hours to work passively on your goals.

In a study by the Brigham and Women's Hospital in Boston, two large groups attempted to remember a person's name with a corresponding picture of their face. Both groups were tested 12 hours after studying to determine their ability to match the names with the faces. Only one group was allowed to study immediately prior to going to bed. **The study revealed huge improvements in memory with the group that rested immediately after studying versus the group that did not.**

This is because during sleep, our brain creates the neurological connections that enable us to retain information. When we are awake, we process our thoughts and memories in the portion of the brain referred to as the "hippocampus." However, the brain's cortex is critical to memory and is very active when we sleep. Activating the cortex while information is still fresh in your mind will ensure you remember more.

Therefore, always review things you need to remember or questions you need answered but cannot figure out before bed. It allows your subconscious mind to work on a problem or help remember information. A great example is to read one of the other *Understand Soccer* series books like *Soccer Dribbling & Foot Skills* to spend the next 8 hours or so allowing your subconscious mind to make you a better soccer player.

Also, you can review information before bed to help you study for quizzes, tests, and exams. To achieve better grades in school, it is far better to work smarter, not harder. **By reviewing the information that you will soon be tested on, you can study less and improve your grades.** Think about what this means: If you study right before bed, then you will have more time to do the things you want to do, like playing soccer or spending time with friends. Studying right before bed will mentally tire you and make it easier to fall asleep, too.

In conclusion, review the questions you need answers to and the information you need to remember before bedtime.

Having the information fresh in your mind when falling asleep will make it easier for your brain to create the connections needed to remember the facts. Finally, studying is the mental equivalent of "working out" your brain. Tire your brain out before bedtime, so you will have a productive and restful night's sleep.

Chapter 9

The Best Temperature for Sleep

Ever have nights in the winter when it is so cold that your body wakes you up to put more covers on? Ever have nights in the summer when you cannot fall asleep because it is so hot that you feel like you are sweating in bed? When the temperature is too cold or too warm in your bedroom, it can be difficult to fall asleep and stay asleep.

According to Michael J. Breus, who is more commonly known as the "Sleep Doctor," **he recommends a sleeping room temperature of 65°F.** For the elderly and infants/toddlers, the best temperature is around 68°F. However, these are recommendations and may vary from person to person. Therefore, it is highly recommended that if you can change the temperature, set the sleeping temperature at different temperature each week for a month or two and see which range allows for the best sleep.

A cooler room temperature will make it much easier to sleep the entire night. **Experts from the American Academy of Sleep Medicine say that you should think of your bedroom as a cave. Your bedroom should be cool, quiet, and dark.** By comparison, bats are found in caves with cool temperatures and can sleep for up to 16 hours per day, so take note of them!

According to WebMD's article titled "What Happens to Your Body When You Sleep," your body temperature will go up and down throughout the day by 2-3 degrees, and your body's coldest temperature naturally occurs at nighttime. **Excitingly, not only can colder sleep temperatures help you fall asleep faster; they can also help you burn more excess fat, regulate your hormones, and boost your metabolism.**

Some tips for sleeping better in the **summer** when your room is too warm are:

-For ambient noise and to keep your room cool, turn on a fan. Point the fan away from your bed to avoid problems with your sinuses.

-Sleep at the lowest level in a multi-story home since heat rises.

-Use sheets instead of thick covers to keep your body temperature down if you must sleep with covers.

Some tips for sleeping better in the **winter** when your room is too cold are:

-Wear socks to keep your body warm
-Have thicker covers
-Wear layers to keep the heating bill down

Remember, a temperature of about 65°F is best to obtain a terrific night's sleep. Not only will this make it easier for you to stay asleep, but it will also increase your metabolism and reduce your bodyfat. Keep your bedroom dark, cool, and quiet to have a terrific night's sleep every night.

Chapter 10

How to Pick a Pillow

Are you a sleeper that has a very large pillow? Are you a sleeper that has used the same pillow for years and now it is very thin? Do you have a specially made pillow? Well, similar to sleeping temperature, there is no "one size fits all" perfect answer for the pillow you should use. However, there are general guidelines that work for most. As with any recommendations in this book, implement the advice, see if it works well for you, and continue trying new things until you find what works best for you.

A good sleeping posture is key to sleeping well. Your pillow helps to support a healthy sleep posture. **Therefore, the biggest thing to remember when selecting a pillow is how is my body/spine aligned?** If your neck and shoulders are not supported, overly supported, propped at an angle that causes twisting, craning, or crunching, your spine and body will not be in alignment. Misalignment causes discomfort in your neck, shoulders, back, while also causing sleeplessness. Let us discuss the three keys to picking a great pillow:

1.Age of the pillow

2.Your natural sleep position

3.The pillow's fill

If you are using a pillow that is several years old, you are likely not obtaining the needed support for restful sleep. Remember, a pillow is used for about eight hours each night. Over two years, that is almost 6,000 hours of use. Like your mattress, your pillow is an investment in high-quality rest, which pays off when you feel alive and awake each day after a restful night's sleep.

Take a quick look at your pillow without the pillowcase on it. Does your pillow have stains? Does it stink or smell even a little? Is any portion of it ripped? These are all signs that your pillow should be replaced. Pillows collect dead skin cells, mildew, mold, fungus, and dust mites. These organisms can cause allergies and impact your breathing while sleeping.

Remember, the position you sleep in should have an impact on the pillow you select. **Back sleepers benefit from thinner pillows that limit stress on the neck, or pillows with middle indentions to maintain the natural curve of the spine. Stomach sleepers require the thinnest pillows of all to keep their spine as straight as possible and minimize the awkwardness of front-sleeping that causes stress on the lower back. Side sleepers sleep best with pillows that are harder and have high loft to ensure your head is well-supported.** A pro tip is to consider placing a pillow between your knees to help maintain spinal alignment as a side sleeper while you rest. Notice how, in the following image, your body's spine is naturally curved. This alignment is what should be maintained while you sleep.

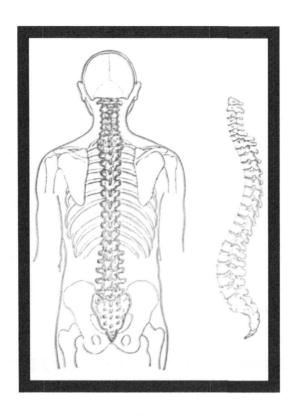

Finally, pillow fill is important for those who suffer from allergies. Types of fills vary drastically from pillow to pillow. For a natural choice, consider feathers. Also, there are synthetic pillows using rayon, foam, or latex. Manufacturers even make hypoallergenic pillows, too. You may be wondering why cost was not a factor in the list of things to consider when picking a pillow. This is because the more "expensive" pillows are well under $100. **Given that you will spend almost 6,000 hours using the pillow, spending $50 or so on a pillow does not seem unreasonable.**

My preferred pillow of choice is the **Core Products Tri-Core Cervical Support Pillow**, which is available on Amazon. This non-allergenic, chiropractor-approved, polyester-filled pillow will ensure your cervical discs (i.e., the portion of your spine along your neck) are comfortable. This pillow has an indentation in the middle of the pillow that cradles your head. Thicker edges fill the hollow between the base of your skull and the top of your back, which takes pressure off your neck. This pillow is more likely to prevent you from tossing and turning in the middle of the night because your head will be in the middle cavity of the pillow.

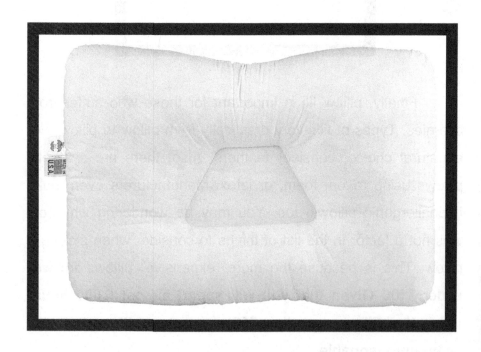

As full disclosure, I have no association with this brand of pillow and receive no benefits from recommending it. I simply enjoy this pillow the most and therefore recommend it to you—assuming you are back sleeper. Otherwise, if you are a side sleeper, then consider a thicker pillow to ensure your neck is level, and your spine is not in a compromised position. I will explain more in a later chapter about which sleeping position is better, but for now, I will tell you that if you become a back sleeper, you will thank me for a better night's sleep—especially when you are older and have less spinal/back issues than your friends.

Things to Remember:
-Replace your pillow every couple of years.
-The position you sleep in should determine the size and firmness of your pillow.
-Picking the proper pillow is an investment in a great night's sleep.
-The pillow's fill (e.g., hypoallergenic vs. feathers) can make a big difference if you have allergies.
-Memory foam is warmer vs. latex, which is cooler.

Section 4 – Sleep Time

Chapter 11

Recommended Hours Per Night

With most things in life, there is no one-size-fits-all approach to how much sleep you need every night. For example, if you have a great mindset towards feeling well-rested after sleep, you have no exams or games the next day, and you are a 25-year-old adult, then you can likely do well with less than the recommended eight hours. However, if you are a 15-year-old with a game the next day, you often feel mentally foggy, and you have a presentation to give in one of your classes, then you need at least the eight hours of recommended sleep to make sure you are mentally sharp.

Things that require more sleep:

-*Physically Exhausting Tasks*: Practice, games, weight training, and running

-*Mentally Exhausting Tasks*: Exams, presentations, working on a project, and writing a paper

-*Emotionally Exhausting Events*: An argument with a loved one, a funeral, or a break-up

-*Illnesses*: Cold, flu, stomach virus, and ear infections

-*Age*: Children and the elderly

Age	Optimal Average # of Hours of Sleep
0-8	9-11 Hours
9-12	8-10 Hours
13-17	8-9 Hours
18-65	7-9 Hours
65+	8-9 Hours

According to the graph above, the optimal amount of sleep varies by age. These hours are general guidelines and work very well for most people. By trial-and-error over time, you may discover that you do better with even more sleep. **However, sleeping too long can leave you just as groggy as not sleeping long enough.** For example, if you are a 14-year-old, you should not plan to wake up in 12 hours unless you did not get any sleep the night before, because this exceeds the recommended maximum amount of nine hours for someone your age. Therefore, you should plan to wake up nine hours after falling asleep and use those other three hours to have a more productive day.

In conclusion, the general guidelines in the previous image are terrific to determine how many hours of sleep you should obtain most nights. However, exhaustive activities require more rest for your body. Sleeping an appropriate amount of time increases your chance of reaching REM/deep sleep, which will be discussed more in an upcoming chapter. Also, remember that everybody is different, and every day is different, so test different sleep lengths to see what works best for you.

Chapter 12

Sleeping Positions

To obtain a restful night's sleep, certain sleeping positions are better than others. If you pick the wrong sleeping position, it can cause long-term physical problems that can creep up on you after years of sleeping in a compromised position. This chapter reveals the potential benefits and problems that you may experience based on your sleeping position.

Side Sleepers: There are many ways to sleep on your side. Some side-sleeping positions are much better than others. As discussed in the chapter on picking a pillow, the ideal position is one in which your spine is aligned. If you insist on sleeping on your side, make sure you have a large enough pillow to keep your head at a 90° angle to the pillow, and a pillow between your knees, so your hips remain aligned, too. Also, it is better to sleep on alternate sides than it is to just sleep on one side of your body. Be aware that **sleeping with your body or head resting on your arm can cut off blood flow to that arm and create shoulder immobility issues later in your life.**

Stomach Sleepers: In the front-facing sleeping position (i.e., stomach sleeping), the front of your body is facing the bed. In this position, you should have a very thin pillow because your spine—specifically at the neck—is in a compromised position. If you sleep on your stomach, you will probably have neck problems in the future. **Finally, this position flattens the natural curve of your spine, which can lead to future back**

pain because spine misalignments result in pinched nerves that send pain signals up to your brain to let you know something is wrong.

Back Sleepers: In the final position discussed in this book, your back is facing the bed. There are a few things that back sleepers should watch out for, as well. **Specifically, sleeping on your back is the most likely position to cause snoring.** Additionally, having too thick of a pillow in this position can push your head too far forward throughout the night and lead to neck and upper back pain. For the back-sleeping position, you should have a thin pillow, or a pillow where the center is cut out to ensure your spine stays aligned.

So, which position is best? **Well, because the goal when sleeping is to keep your back in its natural alignment,**

the best position is sleeping on your back. Sleeping on your back reduces back and shoulder pain. Next, sleeping on your back makes it easier for your body to digest food in the middle of the night and reduces stomach problems like acid reflux. Furthermore, sleeping on your back does not require a pillow between your knees, like sleeping on your side does. Let us be honest: If you sleep on your side and start the night with a pillow between your knees, there is a very good chance the pillow will end up somewhere else when you wake up. Most importantly, sleeping on your back enables your spine's curve to remain in place throughout the night.

Even if you sleep in a different position, you can change. Until I was 18 years old, I slept on my side because that was seemingly the most comfortable. However, after learning all the potential problems that come to side sleepers, I simply changed my body's position prior to falling asleep. For the first couple of months, I found that when I would wake up in the middle of the night, I would often be on my side. To correct myself, I would just roll over onto my backside and continue to sleep. After practicing sleeping on my back, I can now go nearly every night without moving at all and keeping my back towards the bed.

Some changes may need to be made if you suffer an injury from training, but back sleepers have it best. If you are not a back sleeper, consider changing your sleeping position to avoid long-term negative effects. Also, if you take a 15 to 20-minute nap on your side, it is not too harmful because you are not spending eight hours laying on your side. However, to ensure a more restful and better night's sleep, make sure your backside is facing the bed.

Chapter 13

How to Turn Your Brain Off to Fall Asleep

Imagine this: You have a championship game tomorrow, and you cannot fall asleep. You lay there, thinking about your game. Seemingly, hours go by without achieving any rest. So, how do you turn your brain off to make sure you are well-rested? To start, you can attempt the military method of sleeping. In Sharon Ackerman's popular book, *Relax and Win: Championship Performance*, she points out that the U.S. Navy Pre-Flight School developed a routine to help pilots fall asleep in under 2 minutes. Pilots often have odd working hours from day to day and need to be able to sleep quickly whenever they have the time to sleep. The pilots trained using the method for a few weeks prior to realizing its full effects but could even fall asleep after drinking caffeinated coffee and while hearing gunfire noises in the background.

The Military Sleeping Method in Seven Steps:
1. Relax your face, including your tongue.
2. Drop your shoulders to release the tension and let your hands drop to the sides of your body while lying on your back.
3. Exhale from your chest.
4. Relax your legs, thighs, and calves.
5. Clear your mind for 10 seconds by imagining nothing.

6.Mentally say the words, "Don't think," over and over.

7.Within a couple minutes, you should fall asleep!

Personally, I use a more streamlined method where I focus on turning off my mind. As a child and young adult, I found it very difficult to fall asleep from a constantly racing mind and worrying about the next day's events. However, by figuring out how to turn off my mind, I have been able to have about 360 great nights of sleep per year. Given that there are 365 nights each year, having restful sleep on 360 of them allows me a large advantage over my competition because I rarely go through the day feeling exhausted and tired. Remember, I am not a sleep doctor. I am simply a person who was able to go from being someone who had a tough time falling asleep most nights to a person who is a better sleeper than anyone else I know by a large margin.

My method to turn off my mind is simply looking up with my eyes shut. Yes, it seems too simple, but by focusing on looking up, you can clear other thoughts from your mind. Also, because you are doing this while your eyes are shut, you will not have any distractions in your room to affect your sleep. This might sound too easy to you, but do not knock it until you have tried it a few times. I can now fall asleep within a few minutes of my head hitting the pillow nearly every night.

Additionally, I can even fall asleep quickly when spending nights out of my usual bed, such as in a hotel room.

In summary, two time-saving methods to help you fall asleep are the Military Method and looking up while closing your eyes. These methods help you turn off the thoughts in your wandering mind to guarantee a restful night's sleep. After all, it is not fun when you lay down to fall asleep with eight hours of time to sleep and end up only obtaining six and a half hours of sleep. These two methods are time savers because they are sleep savers.

YouTube: If you would like to see this chapter in a video format, then consider watching the *Understand Soccer* YouTube video: *How to Fall Asleep Quicker*.

Chapter 14

What Are the Different Stages of Sleep?

According to the Oxford dictionary, **REM sleep is a kind of sleep that occurs at intervals during the night and is characterized by rapid eye movements (REM), more dreaming and bodily movement, and faster pulse and breathing**.

Your brain remains very active while sleeping even though your body is not moving, according to the National Sleep Foundation. Your brain goes back and forth between two different phases: 1. non-rapid eye movement (NREM) sleep - 2. rapid eye movement (REM) sleep. **NREM sleep is when your body improves its immune system, builds bones and muscles, and regenerates tissues.**

Your brain first enters four different stages of NREM sleep, and then goes to REM. From starting sleep down to deep sleep, and finally to REM sleep, is considered one sleep cycle. **The cycles repeat themselves but tend to shorten by the end of the night, when there is less deep sleep and more REM sleep.** This pattern is often why you wake up from a dream; it is because you were just in REM sleep.

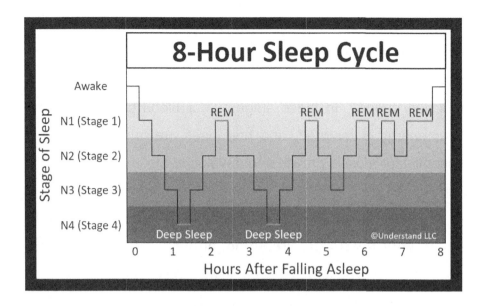

Here are the different stages of sleep:

Stage One sleep is the lightest sleep stage when you can be easily awoken and where you may feel like you are falling or have sudden muscle twitches (i.e., hypnic jerks). Also, as you complete a full sleep cycle and enter REM sleep, this is stage one sleep where you find your body moving from actions you believe you are taking while you are actually asleep. This phase usually lasts for 5 to 10 minutes.

Stage Two sleep is where your heart rate slows down, your muscles relax, and your body temperature decreases as your body prepares to enter deep sleep.

Stages Three and Four are when you experience deep sleep. Your brainwaves slow down, and it becomes more difficult to wake up. If you are woken from deep sleep, you will feel very groggy. In these stages, your blood pressure drops, your energy is restored, and hormones are released that are essential for muscle growth and development.

REM sleep is the final phase of one sleep cycle where your heart rate, breathing, and eye movement speed up. Your brain becomes increasingly active, processing what you have learned while you were awake to help you form lasting memories. Usually, REM sleep happens about 90 minutes after you fall asleep. The length of each REM cycle tends to increase thoughout the night. REM stages typically lasts 10 minutes for your first one. Each of your later REM stages gets longer, and the final one may last up to an hour, according to WebMD. Babies can spend up to 50% of their sleep in the REM stage, whereas adults spend only about 20% of their time there.

The different sleep stages help explain how the sleep cycle works and explain why, for example, if you are in a deep sleep, and a loud noise occurs, you likely will not even hear it. They also explain why we so often wake from dreams.

YouTube: If you would like to see this chapter in a video format, then consider watching the *Understand Soccer* YouTube video: *Different Stages of Sleep*.

Chapter 15

How to Fall Back Asleep

Imagine this: It is 3:30 a.m., and you just woke up because you needed to go to the bathroom. What must you do to ensure you can quickly go back to sleep? This chapter will reveal a few tricks to help make sure your brain stays mostly turned off so that your thoughts do not begin racing, and you do not become fully awake, such as:

1. Barely open your eyes to use the restroom
2. Never turn on a light
3. Keep your alarm clock covered and do not check your phone

First, make sure that when going to the bathroom or waking up for another reason in the middle of the night, be sure to barely open your eyes. The more your eyes "wake up," the more your body will, too. Therefore, open them enough to see where you are going but avoid opening them any more than absolutely necessary. The goal here is to keep your mind foggy, which will increase your chances of quickly falling back asleep.

Second, never turn the light on. Unless you have an absolute pitch-black house, you can see what you need to

view in the middle of the night to use the restroom without needing to use a light. The white light from most light bulbs will make it so your body and brain halts the melatonin production which will make you less tired.

Third, whether you like to do math or not, your mind will probably start performing time calculations if you look at your clock on your phone or alarm clock. Often, if you woke up at 3:30 a.m. and you know your alarm clock is set for 7:30 a.m. you will play mind games like "if I fall back asleep within the next 15 minutes then I will get 3 hours and 45 more minutes of additional sleep and because I fell asleep at 1:00 a.m. that means I will only obtain 6 hours and 15 minutes of sleep. Oh no, I will not get at least 7 hours. I bet I will be tired in the morning..." and so on.

Having a mental dialogue like this will make it very difficult for you to go back to sleep. **Therefore, avoid looking at the clock to avoid the mental gymnastics related to how much sleep you will obtain.** Something I do that helps is to always set two alarms: one with an alarm clock, and one with my phone. Then, I cover them, so I cannot see the time. I will sleep until the alarm clocks make a sound and then I know it is time to wake up. By setting two alarm clocks, this ensures I achieve more sleep—even if I wake up in the middle of the night—and it gives me confidence to know that even if I made a mistake when setting one of them, I have another as a back-up.

Finally, the best way to avoid having to fall back asleep in the middle of the night is to avoid waking up in

the first place. Make sure you do not drink too much water before bed and make sure you empty your bladder prior to bed. Reduce your life stresses or improve your mindset and mental ability to handle difficulties. This will ensure that stress, anxiety, and pressure are not affecting your sleep.

Remember, falling back asleep can be difficult for you if you do not limit the actions that will wake you up in the first place and make it very difficult to fall back asleep. If you avoid making mistakes like opening your eyes fully to use the restroom, turning on a light, and looking at your clock, it will be much easier to fall back asleep.

Section 5 – The Next Morning

Chapter 16

Is the Snooze Button Your Enemy?

Ever hit the snooze button on your alarm clock or phone—only to wake up 5-10 minutes later, feeling even more tired? Ever wonder whether using the snooze button to obtain a few more minutes of sleep is a good thing or a bad thing? I sometimes struggle with this one myself because I am conditioned to hit the snooze button. However, according to Reena Mehra, M.D., M.S., Director of Sleep Disorders Research at the Cleveland Clinic, hitting the snooze button is not helping our bodies achieve the restorative sleep that we need. **She states, *"Much of the latter part of our sleep cycle is comprised of REM sleep (i.e., dream sleep), which is a restorative sleep state. If you are hitting the snooze button, then you disrupt that REM sleep."***

If you fully wake up, then the REM sleep cycle ends. However, if you press the snooze button and go back to sleep, you go back into REM sleep. Because we learned that most sleep cycles last about 90 minutes, when the alarm goes off 5-10 minutes after you press the snooze button, it ends your REM cycle abruptly, which results in a groggy and disoriented feeling.

Dr. Mehra says that if we are disrupting late-stage REM sleep, it can cause a fight-or-flight response, which increases our blood pressure and heartbeat. Increased blood pressure is not supportive of long-term health. Additionally, Dr. Mehra says that if someone is pressing the snooze button, it is likely an indicator that they are not obtaining enough sleep. Just one week of bad sleep can inhibit hundreds of genes in your body, which can lead to heightened stress, lowered immunity, and increased inflammation. These things are not beneficial for a soccer player who is trying to improve in their sport.

To overcome pressing the snooze button, consider:
1. Thinking about the reason you want/need to wake up
2. Buying a better alarm clock
3. Moving your alarm clock as far away from you as possible
4. Going to bed earlier and falling asleep sooner

First, consider the reason you need to wake up. Often activities like a big test you do not want to be late for, having an early morning tournament game, or having a job you do not want to get fired from are all reasons to rise out of bed prior to hitting that snooze button. After all, hitting the snooze button gives us less time to become ready which only increases your morning stress.

For example, when I started my first full-time job, I would set my alarm clock with just enough time so that if everything went well in the morning, I would get to work on time. Then I would hit the snooze button once or twice and be in a panic until I got to work. This created some unnecessary stress that could have easily been avoided by giving myself an extra 10 minutes in the morning and not hitting that pesky snooze button.

Second, consider investing in a better alarm clock. With the advances in technology, there are now alarm clocks that will vibrate your watch/Fitbit to wake you up when you are in a light stage of sleep. How do they determine when you are in a light stage of sleep? Well, the watch/Fitbit detects movement and then will begin vibrating. Do not worry that an alarm like this would wake you up in the middle of the night because you moved. You can set them to only vibrate you awake 15 or so minutes prior to you having your actual alarm clock set for.

For example, if you do not move for 15-30 minutes prior to your alarm clock going off at your set time of 7:30 a.m., then your watch/Fitbit will vibrate at 7:30 a.m. However, if you move at 7:22 a.m., the watch/Fitbit will vibrate because it has recognized that you are currently in light stage of sleep, and you will not feel groggy if you wake up. If you are interested in learning the additional ways that a Fitbit can help you gain confidence and self-esteem, then grab the *Understand Soccer* series book, *Soccer Fitness*.

If having a watch/Fitbit on your wrist or ankle all night does not sound like it will be comfortable, then consider a wake-up-light alarm clock. Even if it is pitch-black outside, this alarm clock's colors will start with a soft dawn red and then shift to a warm orange, and finally to a bright yellow over a 30-minute period. If you are still sleeping when the room is fully lit, then the alarm clock will use sound as a last resort.

Third, make sure your alarm clock is not in reaching distance for you to hit the snooze button without needing to get out of bed. Make sure you physically need to get out of bed to turn off the alarm. In fact, place your alarm on the other side of your bedroom, far away from your bed. Having to get up to turn the alarm off will increase your body's blood flow and will make it easier to wake up without using the snooze function. Therefore, because movement in your body increases your blood flow and alertness, use this knowledge to your advantage. In the morning, force yourself to move so you wake up.

However, if you want to take a nap later in the day, then avoid moving to ensure you can obtain that quick nap. For example, if you had a long drive in the car and are tired and want to take a nap, then stay in the car. Have a small pillow handy and nap away. Bringing all of your things into the house and going to your bed to nap will make it much more difficult for you to fall asleep quickly for a nap.

Finally, go to bed earlier. If you feel tired every morning and feel like you need to hit the snooze button, then there is a good chance you are not obtaining enough sleep. Attempt to shift your bedtime earlier in 15-minute increments, and you might find that it feels a lot easier to get up the first time your alarm goes off.

Remember: Hitting the snooze button impacts your REM sleep. Do yourself a favor and avoid the snooze button by using a few tricks to your advantage. When you hear the alarm clock, remember the things you need to do that day. Additionally, consider purchasing a better alarm clock and place it as far away as possible from you in your room. Also, attempt to achieve more sleep to make it less likely that you will feel the urge to hit the snooze button.

YouTube: If you would like to see this chapter in a video format, then consider watching the *Understand Soccer* YouTube video: *Should You Use an Alarm Clock?*

Chapter 17

How to Feel Good After a Bad Night's Sleep

Ever have a terrible night's sleep? Or a night when you slept well but did not sleep long enough? This chapter will focus on several tips to ensure you feel alert, and your day is not ruined by your previous night's sleep.

Firstly, recall the chapter on "Having Less Rules." **Your mindset/your rules can make a bad night's sleep worse if you have not figured out how to avoid the thoughts that make you tired the next day.** Avoid being like I was for the longest time where if I did not achieve enough sleep, then I constantly thought about how little sleep I had the night before which made me more tired. Become present-minded in whatever you are doing so you forget that you are tired. Can you ever recall a day where you could still perform well even on only a few hours of sleep? Well, it is entirely possible and incredibly easier when your mindset is not working against you and you are living in the present moment of whatever you are doing.

Although this may sound simple, the next tip is to **just drink a glass of cold water**. The cold water will shock your system a bit to make it easier to wake up. Also, drinking cold water in the morning has the following benefits:

-Aids in digestion
-Helps with weight loss
-Prevents and diminishes headaches
-Eases your ability to evacuate your bowels
-Flushes toxins from your system

Additionally, similar to consuming cold water, taking a cold shower will surely wake you up too. Cold showers also help with weight loss and will have you soon forgetting that you are tired because you will be too cold to focus on a night of not enough sleep. Cold showers also reduce sore muscles and aid in recovery after a game.

Furthermore, consider some quick exercise, like stretching or walking. The physical activity will increase the blood flow in your body and to your brain, which will help reduce your tiredness. I will often pair walking with affirmations in the morning to get two things done at once. I even have a 20-minute morning routine to make sure I am starting the day off strong every day. It includes:

1.Gratitude journaling
2.Prayer

3.Taking my vitamins

4.Hanging upside-down to lengthen my spine

5.Jumping on a mini trampoline

6.Stretching

7.Walking

8.Saying affirmations

9.Drinking water

10.Looking at my vision board

I do these even when I have a good night's sleep to give me even more energy to tackle the day. **If the above tips do not work, then consider taking a nap if you have the time.** Reread the chapter on how to nap effectively for pointers to ensure you can shake off the mental fogginess after a bad night's sleep.

Lastly, caffeine can be used to provide a mental pick-me-up. **It is not recommended to consume caffeine regularly because it is addictive and will make you more mentally tired if you stop using it after you have already made using it a routine.** Personally, I only have caffeine maybe once per month before important soccer games or on a day when I did not obtain enough sleep, and the aforementioned tips are not working to wake me up. Better sources of caffeine are tea, coffee, and caffeine pills. If you do not add sugar to your tea or coffee, then it will provide the needed caffeine, in addition to antioxidants, which are beneficial for fighting free-radicals in your body.

Caffeine pills are also good because they do not contain all the additional sugar and additives that many caffeinated drinks have. Avoid carbonated soda pop and energy drinks; even though these have the caffeine you are looking for, they often come with a ton of sugar and artificial ingredients that are very harmful for your long-term health. In most instances in your life, you should avoid placing your long-term health at risk for short-term benefits.

In conclusion, apply what you have learned about having a good attitude when you do not obtain enough sleep. Additionally, drink cold water, take a cold shower, and perform some exercise to get your body and mind going in the morning. If these do not work well enough, then opt for a nap. Only consider caffeine from quality sources as a last resort.

YouTube: If you would like to see this chapter in a video format, then consider watching the *Understand Soccer* YouTube video: *How to Feel Good After A Bad Night's Sleep*.

Section 6 – Bonus Tips

Chapter 18

Six Bonus Tips

Here are six additional tips to help you achieve a full night's sleep:

1. Stay off your phone in bed.
2. Keep a plant in your room for more oxygen-rich air.
3. Stay away from Wi-Fi, Bluetooth, and cell phone radiation.
4. Rapidly open and close your eyes.
5. Avoid using melatonin supplements, since it is technically a hormone.
6. Make sure your room is pitch-black.

First, you should use your bed only for sleeping. Avoid reading, watching television, or eating in bed. **The more things you do in bed, the less your mind will associate your bed with sleep.** Therefore, make sure your body and mind know that once you get in bed, it is time for sleep.

Second, keep a plant in your room for more oxygen-rich air. **Having a plant in your room will increase the amount of oxygen in the air because the plant will use the carbon dioxide you exhale and convert it into oxygen.** Just do not forget to water it!

Third, stay away from Wi-Fi, Bluetooth, and cell phone radiation. Avoid turning on Wi-Fi, Bluetooth, or your cell phone while you sleep. This is because **Bluetooth, Wi-Fi, and cell phones give off very low levels of EMFs/radiation that disrupt cell and brain glucose metabolism, cause oxidative stress of the brain and liver, increase your chances of headaches/fatigue/irritability, increase your blood pressure, and reduce melatonin, which causes sleep disturbances, according to several studies found on the Environmental Health Trust's website.**

Electric and magnetic fields (EMFs) are invisible areas of energy—often called "radiation"—that come with the use of electrical power. Unless you use your phone as an alarm clock, you should avoid keeping your phone in your room due to its Bluetooth signal. Consider changing your phone's settings to airplane mode to ensure the Bluetooth is off and that you will not get any calls or messages throughout the night that may wake you up.

Fourth, rapidly open and close your eyes. By rapidly opening and closing your eyelids for 60 seconds, you will tire out the muscles in your eyelids, which will make you feel more tired than you actually are. **Tired eyes will help you fall asleep faster**.

Fifth, avoid using melatonin supplements, since it is technically a hormone. Avoid using melatonin supplements as a crutch to help you sleep. Melatonin is a hormone that is released in response to darkness and has been linked to the regulation of circadian rhythms. **Although melatonin is not**

addictive, the results of falling asleep quickly by using this hormone can be very addictive. For example, when I was in college, I used melatonin without knowing enough about it first. I started using it only when I really needed to fall asleep fast. However, after it helped me fall asleep so quickly, I began using it most nights and could not fall asleep quickly on the nights I did not take it. I finally realized that I was relying way too much on melatonin, which led me to quit and figure out ways to fall asleep more sustainably instead. Melatonin should be avoided in nearly all instances because it is a short-term fix for the potentially long-term underlying problem of not knowing the right ways to fall asleep quicker and stay asleep longer.

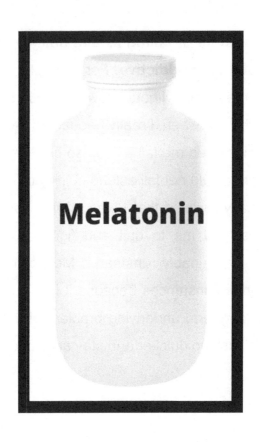

Sixth, make sure your room is pitch-black. Finally, a pitch-black room ensures that no lights will suppress your body's ability to produce melatonin. **Light from manmade lightbulbs act similar to the sun; they both signal your body to continue to create serotonin, which keeps you alert and awake.** Even things like nightlights can make it harder for you to sleep, so avoid those, as well. If light filters into your room from outside the windows, then consider purchasing blackout window shades/curtains, or pinning blankets over the windows to keep the excess light out and ensure a good night's sleep.

Afterword

Considering that we sleep for roughly one-third of our lives, it is vital that we understand how to maximize the quality and quantity of sleep we obtain each night. Making sure that we achieve enough high-quality sleep will provide us with more energy on the field, less mental fog in the classroom, and confidence in the boardroom.

Most soccer players only think about their on-the-field skills when they consider how to become better at soccer. By picking up this book, you have shown that you realize many factors go into being great at soccer. Do not stop improving your soccer knowledge, as there is a considerable amount for every person to know. You have taken the time to read this book, so you have already revealed that you likely care more and are more committed than most other people in the soccer community. Therefore, I applaud you for your efforts and want to let you know that they have not gone unnoticed!

Implement the information revealed in this book to have an immediate impact on your sleep. It is not enough just to read the information; the trick to improvement and positive change is taking massive action. There is no better time than the present to improve your sleep!

Soccer Nutrition:

A Step-by-Step Guide on How to Fuel a Great Performance

Chapter 1

Nutrition Pyramid of Importance

Let us face it, you have only so many hours a day, most of which are spent unrelated to food. As with all things, the more time you spend on something, the more knowledge you will gain, and the better you will become. However, just like how practicing passing and receiving is more important for a soccer player than practicing bicycle/overhead kicks, there are certain aspects of nutrition which will provide bigger results in a shorter period of time. Therefore, make your time count by ensuring that you understand the Nutrition Pyramid of Importance.

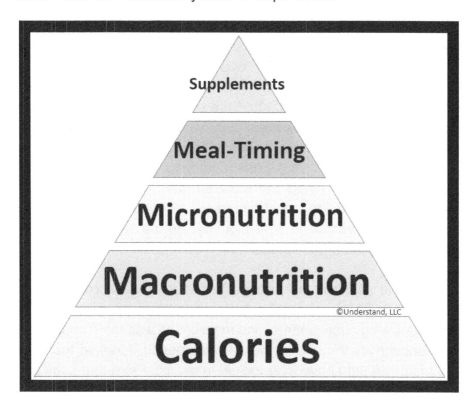

To receive the most from your soccer nutrition, it is so important that you spend time on the more critical areas—like consuming enough calories—and are not so worried about things which bring significantly less value for your time and money. A close friend of mine, Michael Mroczka, would argue with me for years about the number of calories I consume being more important than the quality of those calories when striving to reach a goal. Sadly, sometimes, I can be stubborn and because I had read hundreds of nutrition books, fitness magazines, health encyclopedias, and articles on eating healthy, I believed that eating healthier foods would provide more benefit than watching the number of calories I ate.

Then, three months before my wedding, I hired a dietician to advise me on my eating leading up to my marriage, so I would be in the best shape of my life when I went to Jamaica for our honeymoon. Now, keep in mind that I had been eating extremely healthy and exercising a ton over the 10 years prior—not to mention I had done many at-home DVD workout programs, like P90X, Insanity, Body Beast, etc. Sure enough, the dietician's main aim for my entire 12-week meal plan was focused around making sure I took in the right number of calories for my desired physique and met the guidelines for the macronutrients of carbohydrates, fat, and protein. When hiring the dietician who knew my extensive background in nutrition, I told him to tell me what I needed to do, and not what I wanted to hear him say. So, he stayed consistent about how important the calories and macronutrition were.

I had paid him a lot to guide me, so I was committed to following his advice, no matter how much I thought the quality of the food, taking supplements, and meal timing was more important. Sure enough, at the end of the 12-week period, I looked the best and most defined I have ever looked in my life. From that point on, I realized I was wrong and that the Nutrition Pyramid of Importance was key in determining how I spent my time.

For soccer players, understanding the Nutrition Pyramid of Importance will give you an advantage over players who do not care about nutrition, and players who care about nutrition but focus too much on taking tons of supplements and eating eight times a day.

Let us now discuss each area of the Nutrition Pyramid of Importance and how they will make a significant impact. This is the longest chapter in the book because it will explain the various parts of food to ensure that you can easily follow along with the rest of the chapters.

Calories

When building a pyramid (or your body), having a solid foundation will make it easier to build all other layers. At the base of the Nutrition Pyramid of Importance are calories. A calorie is how we measure the amount of energy there is in food. **Like how producing our world's energy from coal impacts the environment differently than energy from wind, sun, or water, the energy from carbohydrates differs from protein or fat, and a calorie from a candy bar is different when compared to a calorie from organic brown rice.** Here are the recommended guidelines for the number of calories to consume each day:

MALES

AGE	Sedentary	Moderately Active	Active
2	1,000	1,000	1,000
3	1,000	1,400	1,400
4	1,200	1,400	1,600
5	1,200	1,400	1,600
6	1,400	1,600	1,800
7	1,400	1,600	1,800
8	1,400	1,600	2,000
9	1,600	1,800	2,000
10	1,600	1,800	2,200
11	1,800	2,000	2,200
12	1,800	2,200	2,400
13	2,000	2,200	2,600
14	2,000	2,400	2,800
15	2,200	2,600	3,000
16-18	2,400	2,800	3,200
19-20	2,600	2,800	3,000
21-25	2,400	2,800	3,000
26-30	2,400	2,600	3,000
31-35	2,400	2,600	3,000
36-40	2,400	2,600	2,800
41-45	2,200	2,600	2,800
46-50	2,200	2,400	2,800
51-55	2,200	2,400	2,800
56-60	2,200	2,400	2,600
61-65	2,000	2,400	2,600
66-70	2,000	2,200	2,600
71-75	2,000	2,200	2,600
76 and up	2,000	2,200	2,400

Source: Health.gov

FEMALES

AGE	Sedentary	Moderately Active	Active
2	1,000	1,000	1,000
3	1,000	1,200	1,400
4	1,200	1,400	1,400
5	1,200	1,400	1,600
6	1,200	1,400	1,600
7	1,200	1,600	1,800
8	1,400	1,600	1,800
9	1,400	1,600	1,800
10	1,400	1,800	2,000
11	1,600	1,800	2,000
12	1,600	2,000	2,200
13	1,600	2,000	2,200
14	1,800	2,000	2,400
15	1,800	2,000	2,400
16-18	1,800	2,000	2,400
19-20	2,000	2,200	2,400
21-25	2,000	2,200	2,400
26-30	1,800	2,000	2,400
31-35	1,800	2,000	2,200
36-40	1,800	2,000	2,200
41-45	1,800	2,000	2,200
46-50	1,800	2,000	2,200
51-55	1,600	1,800	2,200
56-60	1,600	1,800	2,200
61-65	1,600	1,800	2,000
66-70	1,600	1,800	2,000
71-75	1,600	1,800	2,000
76 and up	1,600	1,800	2,000

Source: Health.gov

If you want to be even more precise, check out: https://www.calculator.net/calorie-calculator.html or simply Google "calorie calculator." Here, you can put in your exact height and weight too, to give you an even closer idea of the estimated guideline for how many calories you should consume each day to maintain your weight. Remember that it can vary from day-to-day, too. **For example, you should eat more on a day where you have a soccer tournament consisting of three games. You should eat less on a day in the offseason when you do not play soccer or exercise.**

Now, you may be thinking that counting your calories can take a lot of time. Yes, it can. I sometimes spent two hours a day preparing/measuring food during my 12-week meal plan prior to getting married. This is too time consuming for most soccer players but understanding how to read a nutrition label (covered in a later chapter), and how to estimate the number of calories and protein that you have eaten in a day will reveal whether your eating habits will help you perform better or hold you back from success.

Macronutrients

Macronutrients are the carbs, fats, proteins, fibers, and fluids needed to function. Macronutrients are needed in large quantities from food. Which ones you consume and when you consume them can be the difference from having a six-pack and lean physique or an average physique which goes unnoticed.

Carbs (carbohydrates) are broken down by the body to provide energy from sugars, starches, and cellulose. For carbs, it is good to classify them into two categories: fast-digesting and slow-digesting. Fast-digesting carbs are the things like white bread, white rice, and white pasta which your body can quickly turn into blood sugar (glycogen), which causes a sharp spike in your body's blood sugar. This can be good when you are about to perform in a soccer game or while drinking a post-game protein shake. However, it can be terrible for your body at other parts of the day when you do not need elevated energy/sugar levels and do not want to experience a "crash" of energy. Foods like oatmeal, whole wheat pasta, sweet potatoes, brown rice, and whole grain bread are much slower digesting and lead to sustained levels of energy without having spikes and dips in energy.

Fats (lipids) are especially important to provide your body energy, support cell growth, protect your organs, keep your body warm, absorb fat-soluble nutrients, and produce important hormones. Fats come in four main types: 1) Monounsaturated 2) Polyunsaturated 3) Saturated 4) Trans. Both monounsaturated and polyunsaturated fats are healthful. Fats from nuts, seeds, olives, algae, and fatty fish will provide the unsaturated fat needed. These types of fats are liquid at room temperature.

Saturated fats are solid at room temperature and can be found in palm and coconut oils, cheese, butter, and red meat. Currently, the health community is torn on whether these are healthy fats or not. Personally, it is hard to say that a coconut is unhealthy for you. There are so many benefits of coconut oil that I could write an entire book on them. Feel free to do additional research on the subject, but I honestly believe based on numerous studies that high-quality organic cheeses, butter, and red meats in moderation will lead to a healthier lifestyle for a soccer player than avoiding them entirely.

Also, there are trans-fats. There are some naturally occurring trans-unsaturated fatty acids in meat and milk fat. **However, the true "villain" of fat is trans-fat, which is chemically created in a factory by hydrogenating oils.** This means that food companies turn liquid oils into solids to increase the shelf life and flavor of the foods which contain them. There is currently a large trend in the fitness industry to avoid these fats because they are linked to heart disease. The trick to seeing if there is trans-fat in a packaged good is to look at the ingredients list for any partially or fully hydrogenated oils and stay as far away from them as you can.

Like carbohydrates, protein can be viewed by how quickly it digests. **First, protein is made up of many amino acids, which help aid in normal cell function, muscle growth, enzyme creation, hormone production, and they can be used for energy.** Whey protein—which comes from milk—is one of the fastest-digesting proteins. It can be purchased separately from milk, too. Casein protein—which also comes from milk—is one of the slowest-digesting proteins. The protein from fish/shellfish is faster digesting than the protein from beef, while chicken/turkey falls in between. Think of protein as your muscle's building blocks.

Lastly, the final macronutrient we will cover is fiber. Technically, fiber is a carbohydrate. However, it is a carb which the body cannot digest. **Fiber is important for regulating digestion, regular bowel movements, helps keep you feeling fuller for longer, improves your cholesterol levels, regulates blood sugar levels, and prevents diseases like diabetes and heart disease.** Fiber is often classified in one of two ways: 1) Soluble 2)

Insoluble. Soluble fiber dissolves in water and in gastrointestinal fluids when it enters your body's stomach and intestines. It changes into a gel-like substance that bacteria in your body digests, releasing gases and a few calories. Insoluble fiber does not dissolve in water or in your body and remains unchanged as it moves through you before being pooped out. Because it is not digested at all, insoluble fiber is not a source of calories your body can use for energy. Think of insoluble fiber as a cleaner which travels through your body scrubbing down the walls and leaving everything a little bit healthier. Soluble fiber is in oat bran, barley, nuts, seeds, beans, lentils, peas, and some fruits and vegetables. Insoluble fiber is in wheat bran, vegetables, whole grains, etc.

If the explanations of each of these macronutrients seemed intense, do not worry. There is an even simpler way to remember what is good to eat and what is not: **If it was made in a factory, then it is probably not good for you**. In general, fruits, vegetables, organic grains, sustainably raised meats, nuts, seeds, beans, and fish are good for you. They can be found in nature. Processed foods, packaged goods, and beverages are made by humans in a factory and usually are not good for you.

Micronutrients

A micronutrient is an element or substance that is required in trace amounts for normal growth and development. **Micronutrients can be broken down into the following key areas: vitamins, minerals, antioxidants, and phytonutrients.** Vitamins and minerals are necessary for good health. Antioxidants, anti-inflammatories, and phytonutrients are not vital, but they are beneficial for recovery, disease prevention, and pain reduction.

Consuming enough vitamins from food and supplements is essential because the body cannot produce enough on its own. **There are 13 essential vitamins, and they are all water-soluble or fat-soluble.** Fat-soluble vitamins can dissolve in fats and oils.

They are absorbed along with fats in the diet and can be stored in the body's fat stores, which makes them the easier of the two for the body to store. Vitamins A, D, E, and K are fat-soluble. Water-soluble vitamins are carried throughout the body but are not stored in the body, so they must be taken in daily. Vitamins B and C are water-soluble.

Minerals are important for your body to stay healthy. Your body uses minerals to build your bones, to engage your muscles, create enzymes, produce hormones, regulate your blood, improve metabolism, and maintain your nervous system. **There are two kinds of minerals: 1) Macrominerals 2) Trace Minerals.** They include calcium, phosphorus, magnesium, sodium, potassium, chloride, and sulfur. You only need small amounts of trace minerals. They include iron, manganese, copper, iodine, zinc, cobalt, fluoride, and selenium. Your body needs larger quantities of macrominerals than trace minerals.

Antioxidants are literally "anti" oxidants. Oxidants are produced inside your body and outside in the environment, and they can react with other elements in your body, such as protein, DNA, and fats. The oxidants will damage your body and cause diseases like cancer, and inflammation like arthritis. Therefore, antioxidants prevent damage from the oxidants. **Antioxidants slow or prevent damage to cells caused by free radicals, which are unstable molecules in your body.**

As an example, if grill marks are burned into your chicken breast because you cooked it on the grill, the burned marks are oxidants in your body. However, if you eat some broccoli and blueberries with the chicken breast, then the antioxidants from the broccoli and blueberries would help fight the oxidants from the burned parts of the grilled chicken.

Antioxidants are mostly found in fruits and vegetables. However, in much smaller amounts, they can be found in nuts, whole grains, and some meats.

Phytonutrients are what give fruits and vegetables their color. Below, the different types of phytonutrients are listed. However, remembering their names is not important. **The key to remembering phytonutrients is knowing the five colors and making sure you are eating each of the colors**:

Red: Protects your DNA while preventing cancer and heart disease.
Foods: Apples, pomegranates, grapefruits, cherries, tomatoes, radishes, watermelons, raspberries, strawberries, etc.

Blue/Purple: Good for heart, brain, bones, and arteries. Fights cancer and promotes healthy aging.
Foods: Plums, red cabbage, beets, eggplants, red grapes, blueberries, blackberries, etc.

Green: Support eye health, arteries, lungs, and liver function. Helps to heal wounds and gum health.
Foods: Broccoli, kale, spinach, collard greens, kiwis, avocados, honeydews, lettuce, celery, etc.

White: Supports bone health, circulatory system, and arteries. Helps fight heart disease and cancer.
Foods: Onions, mushrooms, pears, garlic, cauliflower, parsnips, etc.

Yellow/Orange: Good for eye health, immune function, and healthy development.
Foods: Pineapples, peaches, papayas, bananas, lemons, carrots, pumpkins, sweet potatoes, nectarines, etc.

According to WebMD.com, four out of five people do not eat enough fruits and vegetables. **Although vegetables offer few proteins, fats, or carbs (other than fiber), they are vital for their fiber, vitamins, minerals, antioxidants, and phytonutrients.**

Meal Timing/Frequency

Meal timing is planning meals and snacks for specific times throughout the day (e.g., after a workout) to manage hunger, aid recovery, fuel performance, improve sleep, and build muscle.

Meal frequency is how often you eat. For example, the average person eats three times per day with one snack. However, a soccer player may find it better for their needs to eat five times per day and have a post-workout shake after training.

When meal timing, the most important thing to consider is whether you are consuming a post-workout shake if you are training intensely, and to make sure that you are eating at least three meals per day that contain the number of calories you need to achieve your ideal physique.

Personally, I spent years training hard, eating six full meals per day, and drinking a post-workout shake after every training session. In hindsight, I realize that focusing on some of the soccer-specific skills like the "Big 3" foot skills and an emphasis on passing/receiving would have helped me more in becoming a better soccer player. *(**Note:** If you are interested in the "Big 3" foot skills, which will make the biggest impact on your soccer career, then grab a copy of the Understand Soccer series book, Soccer Dribbling & Foot Skills, to boost your confidence by becoming one of the best dribblers on your team!)*

Supplements

The last area of the Nutrition Pyramid of Importance belongs to supplements. First, a dietary supplement is a product taken by mouth which contains dietary ingredients, like vitamins, minerals, amino acids, herbs, and other substances. As a soccer player, you should be more concerned with soccer than nutrition, so it is important to focus on the few things which will give you the biggest results for the least amount of money and time spent. **Make sure that you are consuming a post-workout shake if you have intense training and want to either maintain your physique or improve it. Also, consume a fish-oil supplement, and a multivitamin.**

With multivitamins, think of them as an "insurance policy." Even if you are eating well, there is a chance you are missing a vitamin or trace mineral in your meal plan which you can easily obtain with an inexpensive multivitamin. Fish oil increases your good cholesterol, lowers your blood fat levels, decreases blood pressure, prevents plaque in the arteries, lubricates joints, and helps with brain development. Can you consume more than these? Absolutely! For years, I did too. However, a post-workout shake, fish oil, and multivitamin is the staple of a successful supplement plan for a soccer player.

To obtain the high-performing body that you want, the order of importance is:

1. Calories
2. Macronutrients
3. Micronutrients
4. Meal Frequency/Timing
5. Supplements

In summary, remember the 80/20 rule for nutrition, which states that 80% of your results come from 20% of the things you do. (**Note:** *If you want to achieve better results in less time, then you will enjoy the Understand Soccer series book, Soccer Mindset, which explains this principle in detail.*) Refer to this chapter or the glossary if you need a refresher on terms used throughout this book.

Chapter 2

Making a Routine

"We are what we repeatedly do. Excellence, therefore, is not an act, but a habit."
—Aristotle

Routines/habits are so important for finding success easily and achieving your goals. When you start something new, there is often excitement, nervousness, and worry. You are stressed about learning something new and must use a lot of mental energy to begin and maintain the process to learn about that new subject. Excitingly, this "10-foot hurdle" that most people place in their minds usually only seems like a 6-inch speed bump after you have gone over it. **Starting, committing, and learning the things you do not know is often the most difficult part of beginning, but once you have the hard stuff out of the way, it becomes much easier from there.**

However, the problem most people face is that they spend so much time and energy the first few occasions doing something which they think every single time will be like that and require a lot of effort. The following image shows how most people view things they know they should be doing, like eating healthy and exercising.

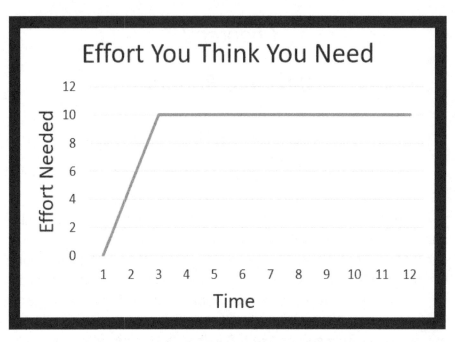

Effort You Think You Need

They give up without realizing they are close to getting to the point where it will be easy to maintain. Therefore, making a routine takes a considerable amount of effort to eat healthy, workout, read, obtain enough sleep, etc. **However, it becomes so easy to maintain once you have created a system (i.e., routine/process/habit).** Instead, look at the following image for what it really takes to keep a routine going.

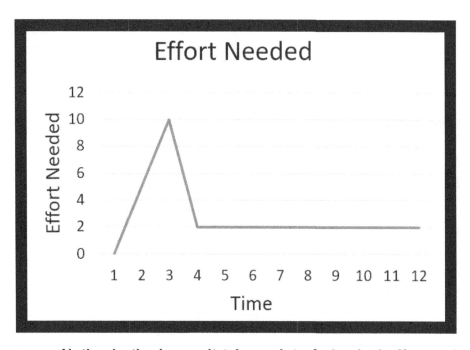

Notice in the image it takes a lot of physical effort and mental energy up front to learn everything and create the habit, but it only takes a bit of maintenance to keep the habit going. So, how long does it take to make a routine stick? Phillippa Lally, a health psychology researcher at University College London, published a study in the European Journal of Social Psychology on how long it takes to form a habit. The study examined the habits of participants over a 12-week period. Each person selected one new habit for the 12 weeks and reported every day on whether they did the behavior and how automatic the habit was.

Because the participants could choose their own habits, some were harder than others. At the end of the 12 weeks, the researchers analyzed the data to determine how long it took each person to go from starting a new behavior to automatically doing it. **On average, it 66 days for the new habit to stick.** It took less time for simpler tasks and longer for more difficult routines. Also, how long it took varied depending on the person and the circumstances. Therefore, 66 days or just over two months is a good target to set up the routine of preparing food and eating healthy. The researchers also found that it did not matter if the participants messed up now and then. Building better habits is not an all-or-nothing process when establishing the routine.

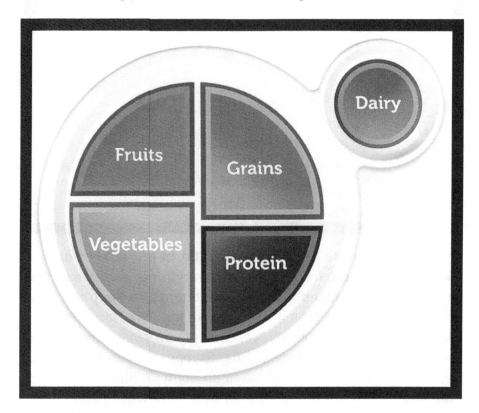

   Given this book is about nutrition for the soccer player, let us talk about the most important routine in nutrition—what to eat and how much of it. The above image of "MyPlate" shows the breakout of how the U.S. Department of Agriculture recommends we portion our meals. **Remember that as a soccer player, your nutritional needs are different compared to the general population given that you exercise a lot more.** More exercise means you need more fuel to perform well and need to know when to eat each type of food to help with recovery without reducing your energy.

Therefore, look at the next image for a better recommendation for a soccer player. Feel free to change it based on your beliefs and what works best for your body.

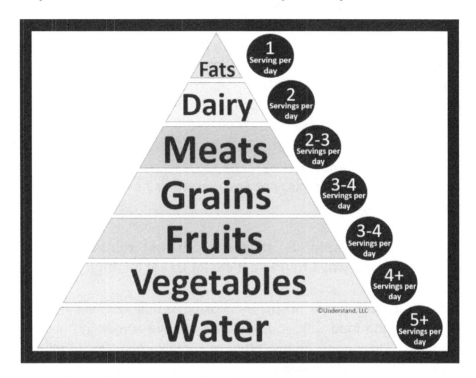

Now, keep in mind that the serving size for an eight-year-old girl will be different than a 15-year-old boy, but fruits and vegetables should be a staple of every meal plan. Notice that the image is a pyramid, instead of a plate. A plate shows that you need to eat the same five food groups in every meal, **whereas the pyramid is not as restrictive and allows you to better plan meals around a training session or game with a serving size equal to one cup.** Also, the pyramid provides a few more things you should consume, including water as the foundation to ensure that your body will remain hydrated. You can be the healthiest eater on your team, but if you are dehydrated before the start of a game, then good luck outperforming someone who may have eaten worse foods but is well-hydrated!

Here are examples of things to eat from each "food group":

Healthy Fats – Coconut Oil, Extra-Virgin Olive Oil, & Avocado Oil
Dairy – Organic Milk, Greek Yogurt, & Minimally-Processed Cheese
Meats/Proteins – Beef, Poultry, Fish, Eggs, Beans, Nuts, & Seeds
Grains – Whole Grain Breads, Rice, Potatoes, Pasta, Organic Corn, & Steel-Cut Oatmeal
Fruits – Melons, Berries, Apples, Pears, Bananas, Peaches, Grapes, & Oranges
Vegetables – Lettuce, Carrots, Onions, Celery, Kale, Cabbage, Broccoli, Cauliflower, & Celery
Water – Not sports drinks, not flavored water beverages, and not soda pop.

Because this chapter is all about creating routines, let us discuss several ways to make it easier to eat healthy:

1. Cook in bulk (meal prep). By cooking in bulk, you will make it easier to bring food with you and always have something healthy prepared. Having so many other responsibilities (e.g., school, work, chores, family, friends, etc.) means that having food already made will make the routine of eating healthy even easier.

2. Keep easy-to-grab fruits and vegetables on hand. Having fruits and vegetables that take minimal or no time to prepare will make eating healthy more enjoyable. Having to prepare something versus grabbing a bag of chips makes it more likely that you grab the chips. However, picking between a bag of chips and an apple will increase your chances of making a more nutritious choice because you do not need prepare an apple, orange, box of raisins, carrots, or celery. For example, when I am in a rush, I can easily grab a banana, a few pieces of cabbage, a slice of organic whole-grain bread, and a handful of nuts. These easy-to-grab items do not need to be prepared; I just have to pick them up and take them with me.

3. Remove unhealthy food from the house. Getting unhealthy food out of your house will make it even easier to eat healthy because you will not need to use any willpower to choose between healthy and unhealthy foods if unhealthy foods are not an option, a concept known as "choice architecture." If you are the person who shops for your family, then make sure you do not go to the grocery store hungry. If you are not the person who shops for your family, then it will be a bit more difficult to get the food that you need. The best thing to do here is to communicate to the person who does the grocery shopping to please buy the healthier and easy-to-grab options you want. However, you may have a parent who does not want to buy healthier foods. Sadly, I had this, and it limited my food choices for a while in the house before my mom began buying foods that I would eat. You owe it to yourself, your health, and your performance on the soccer field to have the conversation with the person who buys the food.

4. Establish a routine for what your "normal" meal should look like. Knowing what a "normal" meal looks like makes it easier to know what should be on your plate. **A great meal involves one vegetable, one meat/protein, one fruit, and one grain (i.e., carb).** Remember this! Honestly, 95% of my meals follow this easy-to-remember pattern, which takes away the hard work of choosing what to eat. If you know that your meals should have four key food groups, then it is easier to prepare/grab them. This habit will help you become a lot healthier and perform better on the soccer field. For example, as I am writing this chapter, I grabbed a stalk of celery (i.e., vegetable), walnuts (i.e., protein), raisins (i.e., fruit), and a sweet potato (i.e., grain/carb) to fuel the two hours of futsal (i.e., 5v5 indoor soccer) which I play on Fridays.

In summary, understanding how long it takes to form a routine, which habits will lead to a healthy lifestyle, and which rules will benefit you can make eating healthier quite easy to do. Remember that most habits take a considerable amount of energy and effort to establish but once created, they are usually easily maintained. Therefore, always do something with the intention of making it a habit. Creating habits like eating healthy, exercising regularly, getting enough sleep, and reading/listening to good books will eventually turn you into the person you want to be.

Chapter 3

Why "Dieting" is Bad

Your relationship with food and how you view it makes a big difference on how you feel and how you look. So many people have "Yo-Yo" diets where they will start a diet for a few weeks, eat a few junk-filled meals, say they need to be better, and then continue eating more meals void of nutrition to cover their poor feelings about falling off their diet. This continues for a few months and then they get back on another diet and change again. Honestly, just trying to explain that is exhausting and the Yo-Yo dieting does not work. It is too difficult to go for long periods of time without the foods you want and then to binge eat them when you slip up.

Instead, what I have found works best is not thinking about it as a "diet." **Rather, think about it as a lifestyle—the way in which you will live.** Because the word "diet" has so many bad feelings and emotions around it for most people, you will be more successful by not viewing your meal plan as a diet. The problem with diets is that they end. Remember the dietician I hired to create a "diet" for me for the 12 weeks leading up to my wedding? Well, he helped me lose 14 pounds. Guess what happened after I went off my diet. I gained 14 pounds in 14 days. I had restricted what I ate for what seemed like forever that I began eating too much once I was off the diet. I swung in the other direction because I was no longer on the diet.

Therefore, it is much easier to have some routines and rules in place which you follow 95% of the time. People often will say *"I dislike having rules because it is so constricting."* If you view it this way, then you are right. However, having some rules like the order you eat your food, ensuring you consume high-quality foods 95% of the time, how much you exercise, etc. actually free you up for other things. As mentioned in the routine chapter, once you have the routine and habit in place, it is so easy to maintain. The rules create freedom because you do not need to spend time and energy deciding on what you should and should not eat. **Rules make it easier to win.** These rules are better referred to as a "lifestyle." Something to do for the rest of your life.

You are one change away in how you view food and exercise from being able to be very fit. Do I still eat burgers, do I eat muffins, do I have cookies near Christmas? The answer is yes to every one of those questions. I have simply just taken the time to figure out my rules which allow me to enjoy life and allow me to feel good about my ability to perform on the soccer field and look good doing it.

After years and years of performing plastic surgery operations, Dr. Maxwell Maltz reveals in his best-selling book, *Psycho-Cybernetics*, that **a person always aligns with their self-image**. This is especially important. People who believe they are overweight can make the choices of an in-shape person over the next few weeks, but they always "snap back" to their view of themselves. Therefore, if they view themselves as a person who will always be overweight, then they make the same poor eating choices and lack of exercise that they always have.

Make sure that you take a minute and ask yourself what your views are related to food, how you feel, how you look, and if you weigh the right amount or too much. Now, it is not to say that it is only "in your head." Saying this would be a bit insulting. Instead, it is based on thought patterns that, when changed, will bring the results you want. As an example, I mentally view myself as someone who will always be healthy and fit. I changed my self-image before I got fit to help achieve the body that I wanted.

To make it easier to align with a "fit" self-image, a trick is to focus on the foods you like. Of all the vegetables out there, my three favorites are carrots, lettuce, and sautéed onions. I love fruits, meats, and most grains/carbs. So, what did I do to be successful? I set up my lifestyle and meal plan focusing on the things I enjoy. Will you ever see me eating an artichoke? Nope. Artichokes disgust me and make my taste buds hurt just thinking about it. Being able to find healthy foods you like will make it winnable to achieve a better self-image.

In conclusion, this chapter is all about challenging how you view your self-image and your lifestyle. If you view it as *"I should be on a diet,"* then you will probably fail. Instead, if you view your food choices as finding what you enjoy and creating a lifestyle, then you will be on your way to success. Having the self-image of a healthy and physically fit person is a great thing. Finally, eating healthy does not need to be difficult; on the contrary, when you eat healthier, all the foods you eat taste better. Imagine eating a slice of watermelon, or another fruit you enjoy. It tastes surprisingly good, right? Now, imagine eating a slice of watermelon after eating two candy bars. It will not taste so good because your taste buds have become used to the sugar rush from unhealthy sweets. Therefore, if you eat healthier foods, then when you eat fruit, it will taste like candy.

Chapter 4

Pre-Game and In-Game Nutrition

Your pre-game meal(s) can set you up for success or can cause you to fail. A person eating a meal comprising steak, cottage cheese, whole milk, cheese, and cashews will have different energy levels than the person who eats carrots, watermelon, fish, and rice before a game. Therefore, let us break down the foods to include in the hours leading up to a game to ensure you have a ton of energy when you need it most.

What to Eat the Morning of a Game

Upon awakening, your body has used up most of its excess blood sugar stores (glycogen) throughout the night, so consume foods that are higher in carbohydrates. Examples are fruits, vegetables, and healthy grains such as quinoa, brown rice, sweet potatoes, steel-cut oatmeal, and organic whole grain bread.

These carbohydrates are beneficial to replenish your body's blood-sugar stores and give you the energy to help you function appropriately until your next meal. There is a common misconception in the athletic world that you are supposed to "carb up" the night before a game. For example, many teams will have a pasta dinner the night before a game, thinking this will help them obtain enough carbs to be fully fueled for the game the next day. It is true that eating some carbohydrates is a good thing before a training session, but you do not need to eat three bowls of pasta the night before a game. **Eating too many carbs the night before a game will increase the chances that they will be stored in the body as fat.**

Also, a good recommendation for the morning of a game is to a consume some protein. However, avoid dairy products! Furthermore, there are better options than nuts, seeds, and beans prior to your game. Instead, eat some eggs or faster digesting sources of protein like chicken, turkey, or fish. Personally, scrambled eggs work best for me because I can prepare them with onions (a vegetable) and make several servings at once. This is great to have as a healthy grab-and-go choice in the morning when you are often hurried and rushed to get out the door.

What to Eat as your Last Meal Before Your Game Starts

It is beneficial for you to consume carbs closer to game time, but this depends on how well your body digests food and how empty or full you prefer to be when playing soccer. **Often, one to three hours before the start of the game is an ideal time to take in more carbohydrates in the form of faster-digesting vegetables, such as carrots; fruits such as apples, bananas, or watermelon, as well as carbs such as quinoa, sweet potatoes, or brown rice. Furthermore, consume turkey, fish, or grilled chicken to ensure you have some protein too and to keep you fuller for longer.** One last thing to consider is that if there is ever a time to add salt to your meal, prior to a game would be the best time to do it. Your muscles need salts which contain minerals like sodium, potassium, and magnesium to contract and work correctly. So, before those long games or games in very warm temperatures, consuming a bit of salt will help your muscles function properly and help you retain more water to ensure you remain hydrated.

Pre-Game Supplement

Many soccer players do not drink a pre-workout/pre-game supplement. However, this is often to the detriment of the player because it can increase their performance by 10-15% and is often used by other players on the field. Many players use lesser versions of pre-workout blends such as carbonated soda pop or energy drinks. The problem with these is all the filler ingredients, artificial flavors, and synthetic preservatives which are not good for your health. You will read more about which pre-workout supplement to take in the next chapter, but understand that it is recommended, and I take one too.

In-Game Nutrition

In 95% of practices/games, you do not need in-game nutrition. **Drinking a sports drink on an extremely hot day when you have a game that lasts more than an hour is acceptable but for most games, you already have enough nutrition in your body if you ate well before the game.** Your body is comprised of 70% water, so drink plenty of it!

As you can see, there are several things to ensure you have energy on game day. Also, this same knowledge can be used when you try out for a team too. If you have a tryout coming up, consider grabbing the *Understand Soccer* series book, *Soccer Tryouts*, to learn all the things that will help you make the team and have confidence from the start without being nervous. For pre-game nutrition, remember that quicker digesting foods like poultry and fish, vegetables, fruits, and grains/carbs are your best bets prior to game time to ensure everything in your system is helping you perform at your peak. Consider a pre-workout supplement to use only before games to give you a boost and do not worry about in-game nutrition other than water.

YouTube: If you would like to watch a video on what to eat before soccer, then consider watching the *Understand Soccer* YouTube video: *What to Eat Before a Soccer Game*.

Chapter 5

Supplements

Pre-Workout/Game

Ever feel like you do not have enough energy to perform well on the field? Well, pre-workout supplements can give you the physical boost and mental jump start that you need. The decision on whether to take a pre-workout supplement prior to a game will vary from person to person. Personally, I will take a high-quality pre-workout supplement to give me additional energy during important games. It is important to have enough energy to show off your skills and abilities. However, given that I am not a licensed physician, please consult your doctor before taking a pre-workout supplement.

Also, keep in mind that at least 80% of the pre-workout supplements on the market are not recommended. They are filled with artificial colors, flavors, sweeteners, and typically have a lot of filler ingredients, which make it seem like you are getting more for your money. However, you are only getting a bunch of chemicals, which will lead to long-term problems.

Instead, go for a pre-workout supplement with only a few high-powered ingredients—the most important being caffeine. **Caffeine is a central nervous system stimulant, which gives you energy and mental focus. Caffeine takes effect about 45 minutes after you consume it.** While caffeine is helpful for your performance on the field, the effects of caffeinated beverages (e.g., tea, coffee, pre-workout supplements, energy drinks, or carbonated soda pop) lasts for 4-6 hours, so avoid consuming caffeine in the 6 hours prior to bedtime to minimize its impact on your rest.

One of my recommended pre-workout supplements is *Pure Pump*. Pure Pump has the trusted ingredients you want in a pre-workout supplement without any of the fluff. This product is for both males and females. I am not sponsored by this company; I just really like this product because they do not add unnecessary ingredients. Personally, I consume the unflavored version, but I recommend the flavored version because the unflavored version tastes a bit metallic. One scoop works well for children, and two scoops is the recommended serving size for an adult.

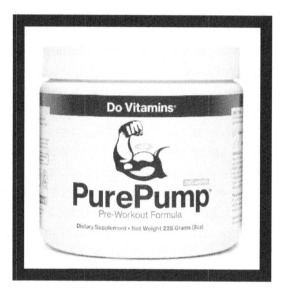

When you take any kind of pre-workout supplement, make sure to drink at least eight ounces of water with it.

Post-Workout/Game

Ever wonder what would help you best recover after a training session, practice, or game in that 30-minute window when your body really wants nutrition to grow stronger? **Well, foods that are good to consume after a game are foods high in carbohydrates and fast-digesting protein.** An example of a food that is easy to obtain is organic milk. Though the evidence shows altering views on lactose, having some organic milk or a whey protein shake with non-GMO dextrose is beneficial after a game. You want to take in enough carbohydrates to spike up your blood sugar after a practice, game, or workout so that your body uses the protein that you will take in.

In terms of a supplement to use, **whey protein isolate is recommended because it is one of the most bio-available and quickest digesting proteins.** (Whey protein concentrate is less expensive, but it has a lot of fat and lactose that can lead to smelly flatulence. Whey protein hydrolysate is the best, but it is almost double the price of whey protein isolate. Whey protein hydrolysate does not provide even close to twice the benefits of whey protein isolate and should only be considered if cost does not matter to you.) If you drink milk, it has milk protein, which is 20% whey protein and 80% casein protein. It is essential that if you have more physical activities later in the day, take in enough carbohydrates like dextrose, bread, rice, potatoes, pasta, and oatmeal to replenish your glycogen. It is critical to minimize the amount of fat and fiber that you take in during the post-workout 30-minute window because fiber and fat are slower digesting. They slow the absorption of vitamins, minerals, and nutrients. Avoid very dense foods like spinach or peanut butter unless there is absolutely nothing else that you can consume. Something healthy is better than nothing.

The other recommended post-workout supplement is **creatine monohydrate.** More than 1000 studies have shown that creatine is a top supplement for exercise performance. Creatine is a combination of three essential amino acids: glycine, arginine, and methionine. Consuming creatine increases your stores of phosphocreatine, which is a form of stored energy in the cells that helps your body produce more high-energy ATP. ATP is referred to as the body's "energy currency." When you have more ATP, you perform better during soccer. Creatine also helps several processes that increase muscle mass and strength and boost recovery. If you worry about taking something as foreign sounding as creatine monohydrate, then understand that there are one to two grams of creatine in a pound of beef, and varying amounts in other red meats, dairy, poultry, and fish.

If you want to figure out which supplement you are interested in, check out labdoor.com! They go through most supplements and do the research on which ones are healthy and which ones are not, so you can have more time for soccer.

General Health

To maintain health and wellness, the last two things to consider are a multivitamin, and a fish-oil supplement. Think of a multivitamin as "insurance." By following the tips in this book and eating healthy food (e.g., fruits, vegetables, meat, grains, and dairy), you will obtain the vitamins and minerals you need. However, just in case there is a certain food that you are not eating with nutritional value that is not found in other foods, a multivitamin can help make up for what your meal plan lacks.

Lastly, a fish oil supplement is good too. Fish oil has been shown to:
1. Support heart health.
2. Treat mental disorders.
3. Aid in weight loss
4. Support eye health.
5. Reduce inflammation.
6. Support healthy skin.
7. Reduce liver fat.
8. Reduce depression.
9. Reduce attention deficit disorders.
10. Improve asthma.
11. Help bone health.

In summary, a pre-workout supplement increases your energy for important games and tryouts. Post-workout supplements like whey protein isolate and creatine increase strength and muscle building while shortening the time to recover.

Finally, a multivitamin acts as a great way to not worry about missing any key nutrients in your meal plan while fish oil helps with so many things that it is an important part of overall health and wellness.

Chapter 6

Post-Game Nutrition

After your game is done, and you took a post-game supplement, your body is primed to use the nutrition that you consume to repair itself and build your muscles. Soccer players have practice and/or games several times per week, so it is ideal to take in nutrition that will help your muscles recover faster and ensure that you are not fatigued before the start of your next game.

Consume a meal like the one you ate hours before the game started. Include one meat, one fruit, one vegetable, and one carb/grain to help your body recover from the intense game. If you do not feel that you worked hard enough in the game to eat all this food, then consider eliminating the carb/grain. **If you eat well after your game, then you will perform better, quicker, and more efficiently next time.**

Before bed, you want a slower digesting meal, so consume foods high in fiber, high in fat, and high in protein. Some things to consider eating are nuts, seeds, meat, different nut butters (almond, cashew, and to a lesser extent, peanut butter). Also, vegetables are always great to eat. Personally, I eat five servings of vegetables a day because they help keep you full for longer. Vegetables contain vitamins, minerals, antioxidants, and phytonutrients which help you recover quicker, keep you feeling better, and help to maintain steady blood sugar levels so your energy levels do not spike and crash. Additionally, if you choose to eat dairy products and are not lactose intolerant, then before bed is one of the two best times to consume them.

Cheese, Greek yogurt, whole milk (preferably organic), and cottage cheese will do a terrific job of supplying muscle-repairing nutrients to your body for most of the night. **Dairy's milk protein is made up of 20% whey protein, and 80% casein protein. Casein protein takes up to seven hours to digest, which makes it a great pre-bedtime protein to help your body recover and gain strength.** Avoid food with a lot of carbohydrates (i.e., carbs) right before bedtime because the carbohydrates can spike your blood-sugar, which can make it harder to fall asleep and increase the chances that the food you just ate will be stored as fat, rather than used as fuel.

Example Meal Plan for a 3 p.m. Game

Breakfast (8 AM):
3 eggs (protein & fats)
½ sautéed onion (vegetable)
½ cup of oatmeal (carb)
1 orange (optional fruit/carb)

Lunch (noon):
8 ounces of grilled chicken breast (protein)
1 cup of carrots (vegetable)
1 apple (fruit/carb)
1-2 slices of organic bread (carb)

Snack (as needed):

1 banana (fruit/carb)
2 organic rice cakes (carb)

<u>Pre-Workout (30 mins before game time):</u>
1-2 scoops of pre-workout (additional energy)
1-2 cups of water (muscle recovery and hydration)

<u>Game (3 PM)</u>

<u>Post-Workout (5 PM):</u>
1 scoop of whey protein isolate (muscle recovery and growth)
1-2 cups of milk or water (muscle recovery and growth)
5 grams of creatine (muscle recovery and growth)

<u>Dinner (6 PM):</u>
8 ounces of turkey, beef, chicken, or fish (protein & fats)
1 cup of broccoli (vegetable)
1 cup of blueberries (fruit/carb)
1 sweet potato (carb)

<u>30 Minutes Before Bed (10 PM):</u>
½ cup of nuts (protein & fats)
4 ounces of organic cheese (protein & fats)
1-2 cups of leafy greens (vegetable)
1 cup of Greek yogurt or cottage cheese (protein & fats)

Example Meal Plan for a Daylong Tournament with 3 Games

<u>Breakfast (5:30 AM):</u>

3 eggs (protein)
½ sautéed onion (vegetable)
½ cup of oatmeal (carb)
1 orange (fruit/carb)

<u>Pre-Game (30 mins before game time):</u>
1 scoop of pre-workout (additional energy)

<u>Game (7 AM)</u>

<u>Snack (8:45 AM):</u>

1 banana (fruit – carb)
2 organic rice cakes (carb)

Pre-Game (30 mins before game time):
½ scoop of pre-workout (additional energy)
1 cup of water (muscle recovery and hydration)

Game (11 AM)

Lunch (1:00 PM):
8 ounces of grilled chicken breast (protein)
1 cup of carrots (vegetable)
1 apple (fruit/carb)
1-2 slices of organic bread (carb)

Pre-Game (30 mins before game time):
½ scoop of pre-workout (additional energy)
1 cup of water (muscle recovery and hydration)

Game (3 PM)

Post-Game Shake (5 PM):
1 scoop of whey protein isolate (muscle recovery and growth)
2 cups of milk or water (muscle recovery and growth)
5 grams of creatine (muscle recovery and growth)

Dinner (6 PM):
8 ounces of turkey, beef, chicken, or fish (protein & fats)
1 cup of broccoli (vegetable)
1 cup of blueberries (fruit/carb)
1-2 cups of whole wheat pasta (carb)

30 Minutes Before Bed (9:30 PM):
½ cup of nuts (protein & fats)
4 ounces of organic cheese (protein & fats)
1-2 cups of leafy greens (vegetable)
1 cup of Greek yogurt or cottage cheese (protein & fats)

*Note: This is a great meal plan for an adult. If you are a child or are reading this to help your child, then cut the portion sizes roughly in half. Make substitutions where necessary based on food preferences. Each section is labeled (i.e., protein, vegetable, fruit, carb) to make it easier for you to switch out something you or your child does not like. For example, use fruit interchangeably and vegetables too (i.e., eating watermelon instead of a banana is terrific and so is eating celery instead of broccoli.)

YouTube: If you would like to watch a video on what to eat after soccer, then consider watching the *Understand Soccer* YouTube video: *What to Eat After a Soccer Game*.

Chapter 7

Ronaldo's and Messi's Meal Plans

For an effective meal plan, it is often important to look at some of the best players to uncover what they are eating and to use it as a guideline for what you should eat. Specifically, if you saw your favorite star eating junk food before games, you might be more likely to believe that eating healthily does not matter too much. However, if you see the best players having a well-balanced meal plan, then it is more likely that you will follow their advice to improve your game. Let us look at what Cristiano Ronaldo and Lionel Messi consume to stay at the top of their game. For Cristiano Ronaldo, we will look at what he eats over the course of a typical day. For Lionel Messi, you will read how he changes up his meal plan depending how far away is his next big match.

Cristiano Ronaldo's Daily Meal Plan

From extensive research of Cristiano Ronaldo's eating habits, as shown in the images on his Instagram account, he divides his daily food intake into five to six smaller meals to prevent weakness or hunger throughout the day and provide protein to ensure he can maintain and build muscle. His favorite source of protein is seafood, but he also consumes protein shakes, steak, turkey, chicken, and eggs too. **Ronaldo changes his breakfast foods depending on the demands of training/games**, but he has been known to eat whole-grain cereal, egg whites, fruit juice, coffee, cold cuts, cheese, avocado toast, and fruit. For his first snack of the day, Ronaldo often enjoys fish and bread.

For lunch, Ronaldo likes fish or chicken, whole-wheat pasta or a baked potato, and green vegetables. For his second snack of the day, he keeps it quick by consuming a protein shake to promote muscle recovery after his vigorous training. For dinner, Ronaldo often enjoys his favorite meal of Bacalhau à Brás. It is a Portuguese dish made from salted cod, onions, potatoes, scrambled eggs, black olives, and fresh parsley. From time to time, Ronaldo also eats salads, rice, and beans. Again, he does not consume all these foods in one sitting, but he does eat high-quality foods like these to ensure that he performs well and recovers quickly.

Now, though this is a nutrition book, do not be misled into believing that he eats nothing unhealthy because he will celebrate birthdays with cake and occasionally has chocolate too. Therefore, if 95% of your meals are healthy, a slice of cake will not hold you back too much. However, should you want to avoid eating junk foods, you will have an advantage over those who do. **Also, because one of the main concepts of this book is to make things winnable, consider having dark chocolate instead of milk chocolate to make sure you are getting plenty of**

antioxidants while you satisfy that chocolate craving. Similarly, find organic cake mix when baking a cake to know that the ingredients are better than the generic pre-made cake which has 50+ ingredients—many of which are difficult to pronounce.

Lionel Messi's Weekly Eating Plan

Now, let us break down Lionel Messi's meal plan, according to Men's Health Magazine. **A week before a match, Messi decreases his carbohydrate intake and increases the amount of protein and water he consumes.** Also, Lionel Messi eats vegetable soup with spices at the beginning of meals. Some spices Messi uses are chili powder, coriander, ginger, and turmeric. Without as many carbohydrates, Messi may experience slightly less energy in the days leading up to a game. Cutting carbohydrates forces his body to become more efficient with the sugar levels in his blood.

Once Messi reintroduces carbohydrates a day before the game and on the day of the game, it increases his energy because of the carb loading. Messi's ideal dinner the day before a game contains meat (e.g., fish, chicken, or prawns), green veggies, an orange, and potatoes. Six hours before match time, Messi eats porridge and egg whites. Then, 90 minutes before the game starts, Messi eats fruit. Now, do you need to go to this extent by starting a week before each game to see results? Probably not. However, understand that the more you take eating seriously, the more it will help improve your in-game performance.

So, do you see any similarities between Ronaldo and Messi? They both eat healthy foods knowing that it will fuel their performances to ensure they will be the best. If you are wondering how top athletes like Cristiano Ronaldo train in the gym and on the pitch, be sure to grab the *Understand Soccer* series book, *Soccer Fitness*. Here is a summary of Ronaldo's & Messi's meal plans should you want to glance back at them quickly:

Cristiano Ronaldo

Sample Breakfast:
Whole-grain cereal, egg whites, and fruit

Sample Snack #1:
Tuna roll with lemon juice

Sample Lunch:
Chicken salad, green vegetables, and a baked potato

Sample Snack #2:
Protein shake

Sample Dinner:
Turkey, beans, rice, and fruit

Lionel Messi

1 week before a big match:
Meat (fish, chicken, or prawns)
Green veggies
Vegetable soup with chili powder, coriander, ginger, and turmeric

The day before a big match:
Meat (fish, chicken, or prawns)
Green veggies
Orange
Potatoes

Six hours before match time:
Porridge
Egg whites

90 minutes before the game starts:
Fruit

YouTube: If you would like to watch a video on what Lionel Messi eats leading up to a game, then consider watching the *Understand Soccer* YouTube video: *Lionel Messi Meal Plan*.

YouTube: If you would like to watch a video on what Cristiano Ronaldo eats throughout a day, then consider watching the *Understand Soccer* YouTube video: *Cristiano Ronaldo Eating Diet*.

Chapter 8

What to Eat on Non-Training/Playing Days

After reading about foods to eat before and after training, let us discuss what to eat on non-training days. A non-training day is an off day where you do not have weightlifting, practice, intense conditioning for at least 30 minutes, or a match. On these days, you need less energy from food but still want to avoid being hungry and recover fully.

Dairy (cheese, Greek yogurt, whole-fat milk, and cottage cheese) takes a long time for your body to digest, so the best times for a soccer player to eat it are as part of your last meal of the day after all activity or on off days where you are not training. Milk sugar, lactose, is a complex sugar which is tough to digest and more time consuming than simple sugar for your body to breakdown. Also, since milk protein is 80% casein protein, which is the slowest digesting protein that takes up to 7 hours to digest, it is best to avoid dairy before physical activities. Remember, food is fuel. Be sure to use the quicker digesting foods before and immediately after games and keep the slower digesting food for when you go long periods without eating, the most obvious one being when you go to sleep.

      You will learn more about the macronutrients I aim to eat on off days, but I eat fewer carbs since I do not need as much energy on off days. Furthermore, I eat more fat to ensure I stay full, even though I have consumed less food. Similarly, I tend to eat around 3,600 calories per day on days I exercise and only 3,000 calories on days I do not work out to ensure my body has the energy to perform when I am competing. So, what does this mean for you? **Well, be sure to eat more food on training days to improve performance and help recovery but reduce the amount you eat on off days to ensure you stay at a good body composition.**

      Additionally, the reason you want to eat more fats is not only to stay full, but to fight inflammation. Inflammation occurs in your joints, ligaments, tendons, spine, etc. anytime activity occurs. So, after days where you exercised intensely, your body will be suffering from inflammation which creates physical pain and increases the time your body should spend resting instead of preparing for the game you love. As a result, eating more inflammation fighting fat will make it easier to become fully recovered and get back on the field. According to *Harvard Health Publishing*, trans fats increase inflammation in the body, so we want to focus on the unsaturated fats with anti-inflammatory properties, according to the *American Journal of Clinical Nutrition*. **Consume fats like nuts, fish/fish oil, and olive oil to fight inflammation.**

Nuts like almonds, walnuts, and pistachios are high in protein, fat, and fiber and have unsaturated fats, which help lower your bad cholesterol and raise your good cholesterol. **Fish oil has omega-3 fatty acids, which help keep your blood-fat levels in a good range, reduce stiffness, lessen the effects of asthma, increase focus, and decrease joint pain.** Lastly, a study published in the *Journal of Nutritional Biochemistry* found that the oleocanthal in olive oil had a significant impact not only on chronic inflammation but also on acute inflammatory processes, similar to the effects of nonsteroidal anti-inflammatory drugs (NSAIDs) like aspirin or ibuprofen (Motrin/Advil). Therefore, you can obtain the same inflammation-reducing properties from olive oil as the unnatural, over-the-counter medications, which have negative long-term side effects, especially on your liver.

Furthermore, if you are a person who is always looking for ways to get an edge over your competition, stretching on your off days is a great way to keep your muscles flexible, have healthy joints, reduce your chance of injury, and improve recovery. **Stretching helps in the recovery of muscles by lengthening them and increasing the amount of blood flow to them to take away the lactic acid. Lactic acid is created when you use your muscles past the point they are used to working, which**

creates muscle soreness the next day or two. If learning more about stretching interests you to improve your recovery and dominate on the pitch, then grab the *Understand Soccer* series book, *Soccer Fitness,* to learn more. Also, very mild exercise like walking will help to rid your body of its soreness too.

In summary, the best time to consume dairy is as part of your last meal of the day assuming you are done with all physical activity or are on an off day. Off days are a great time to reduce your carbohydrate intake because you need less energy. Furthermore, eating more fat on off days in the form of nuts, fish/fish oil, and olive oil will help you remain full and decrease the amount of inflammation in your body which lengthens the time it takes for you to fully recover and get back on the field. Lastly, a bit of stretching and walking will go a long way to helping to improve blood flow to your sore muscles which will cut your recovery time significantly.

Chapter 9

Sports Drinks vs. Water?

So how much water should you drink? According to the National Collegiate Athletic Association (NCAA), here is the recommended amount of water to consume for a college athlete. Reduce the portion size depending on your age:

When:	Ounces:	Ounces-to-Bottles:
2-3 Hours Before Activity	16 ounces	About 1 Regular-Sized Bottle
15 Minutes Before Activity	8 ounces	About 1/2 Regular-Sized Bottle
During Activity	4 ounces every 15-20 minutes	About 2-3 Large Gulps (1/4 of a Regular-Sized Bottle)
After Activity	16-20 ounces	1 to 1-1/4 Regular-Sized Bottles or 1 Large Bottle

Remember, how much you should consume depends on the weather conditions, and your level of activity on the field. Specifically, if you are a goalkeeper playing in the cool weather of a late-fall game, then drinking a lot of water is not as important. The colder temperature will limit the amount you sweat, and goalkeepers are the least-active players on the field. However, if you are an outside midfielder who runs a ton, and you are playing in the hot summer sun, then you should double or triple the amount of water you consume at halftime during a game.

When you sweat and do physical exercise, your body uses electrolytes. Although that may seem like a complex word, an electrolyte is a type of salt. Sodium, potassium, chloride, calcium, magnesium, and phosphate are all common components of electrolytes. **Electrolytes are essential for nerve and muscle function; they participate in regulating bodily fluids, and they help control blood pressure.** With this knowledge, many companies have created products aimed at aiding athletic performance. In theory, these drinks should help improve your performance, but let us look at what is really in a sports drink, and whether drinking one while playing helps. Here is the label of a bottle of the leading sports drink brand:

Nutrition Facts

1 servings per container

Serving size   Bottle (1g)

Amount Per Serving

Calories   **140**

	% Daily Value*
Total Fat 0g	0%
Saturated Fat 0g	0%
Trans Fat 0g	
Cholesterol 0mg	0%
Sodium 270mg	12%
Total Carbohydrate 36g	13%
Dietary Fiber 0g	0%
Total Sugars 34g	
Includes 34g Added Sugars	68%
Protein 0g	0%
Vitamin D 0mcg	0%
Calcium 0mg	0%
Iron 0mg	0%
Potassium 80mg	2%

* The % Daily Value (DV) tells you how much a nutrient in a serving of food contributes to a daily diet. 2,000 calories a day is used for general nutrition advice.

Ingredients: Water, sugar, dextrose, citric acid, natural and artificial flavor, salt, sodium citrate, monopotassium phosphate, modified food starch, glycerol ester of rosin, blue 1.

The Good:

It has water and a few electrolytes (salt, sodium citrate, and monopotassium phosphate).

The Bad:

Sugar – It has a lot of sugar which is only helpful if you are exercising strenuously for at least 60 minutes or more.

Dextrose – A faster-digesting form of sugar that is immediately usable by your body. Again, unless you are exercising intensely for at least an hour, you do not need it.

Citric Acid – Adds flavor and acts as a preservative.

Artificial Flavors – Synthetic chemicals that cost less to produce than finding natural sources.

Modified Food Starch – Most commonly derived from genetically modified corn, then altered to give it a more desirable texture.

Glycerol Ester of Rosin – a synthetic oil-soluble food additive known as "E445" used to keep oil in suspension in drinks.

Blue 1 – Linked to damaging chromosomes which is your genetic material. Each colored sports drink has a different dye which negatively impacts your health.

Next, the *British Medical Journal* has published many articles revealing the truth about sports drinks. Specifically, drink when you are thirsty and do not waste your money or calories on sports drinks—water is the better choice instead. The *British Medical Journal* team uncovered that sports drink makers spent a lot of money sponsoring less-than-rigorous research which suggested thirst was not a good guide to hydration and casting doubt on water as the beverage for staying hydrated. According to Fortune Business Insights, they expect the sports drink market to reach $32.61 billion by 2026. **Therefore, the same companies that are telling us water is not good enough are the same companies that profit when we purchase their sports drinks.**

In summary, water is the doctor recommended drink of choice for athletes. Avoid the overpriced sugar water with a few different types of salts which do not benefit you much and have a lot of unhealthy filler ingredients. Drink as you are thirsty to ensure you remain hydrated.

Chapter 10

General Nutrition Tips

This chapter is a catch-all for things that should be in this book but do not need an entire chapter themselves.

1. Eat your food in order.
2. Food on-the-go.
3. Stay away from alcohol, smoking, drugs, processed food, and fast foods.
4. Use the best salt.
5. Glass containers > plastic containers.

First, most people are only concerned with eating healthy foods, but they do not think about the order in which they should eat the healthy food. Say you have a healthy meal of organic bread, broccoli, chicken, and a banana. Most people eat the bread first because they have not eaten in a while, and their blood sugar is low. They eat most of the bread prior to starting on the other parts of their meal. They take bites of everything; sadly, the broccoli is the last food finished because they know it is healthy, but it their least favorite thing on their plate. **Eating in the order of carb, fruit, meat, vegetable is terrific either right before a game or immediately after a game to increase your energy levels for soccer or increase your blood-sugar levels after a workout to ensure that you use more of your meal to rebuild your muscles.**

However, eating in this order is not optimal for the meals that are far from physical exercise. If you are hours away from exercise or a soccer practice/game, then you should reverse the order in which you eat your food. **You should eat in order of vegetable, meat, fruit, grain. This ensures that you will**

consume the slower-digesting foods first. This will reduce the chance of a blood-sugar spike and ensure that you have a steady stream of energy for the next several hours, prior to eating your next meal. If you eat in the opposite order, and you consume the faster-digesting grains/carbs and fruit first, then your blood sugar will spike, more of the food may be stored as fat, your blood sugar will dip dramatically, and you will become exhausted and have limited energy for the next few hours, until you eat again.

Explained more scientifically, the higher the blood-sugar (i.e., glucose) level in your body, the more insulin your pancreas releases to balance your blood-sugar levels. Insulin also breaks down fats and proteins for energy. **If your pancreas releases a lot of insulin, then it will begin breaking down all your food very quickly, thus giving you a lot of energy for an hour or so. This is great if you will play soccer but bad if you will not be active, because you will feel a large energy crash.** Rapidly changing blood-sugar levels can cause serious long-term health problems, like diabetes.

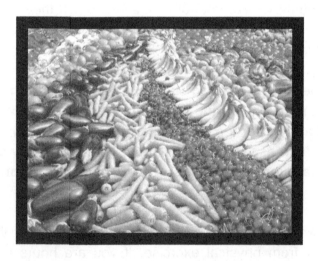

Second, make eating healthy winnable. By having food to grab on-the-go, you increase the chances you make the right food choices. If you are a parent reading this book, consider grabbing the *Understand Soccer* series book, *Soccer Parenting*, for immediately usable information to help your soccer player perform better on the field and to boost your confidence helping them with soccer, even if you have never played before yourself. Here is a chart of healthy foods ready to eat or that take minimal preparation; You will notice that most of the snacks are fruits and vegetables:

Protein Bar	Banana	Blackberries	Pineapple	Parsnips
Organic rice cakes	Apple	Blueberries	Apricot	Cauliflower
Non-GMO Popcorn	Orange	Strawberries	Pear	Mushrooms
Almonds	Grapes	Raspberries	Tomatoes	Broccoli
Peanuts	Raisins	Cherries	Peppers	Carrots
Cashews	Peach	Cranberries	Cucumber	Radishes

Third, there are several things that will make it harder to be a success in soccer and life. **The activities that will prevent you from being the best player you can be are drinking, using drugs recreationally, and smoking.** These are must-avoid habits as they will force you to spend time, money, and mental energy on things other than soccer and impact your health and endurance on the field. Also, though not as obviously bad for you, processed foods and most fast-food restaurants will only slow you down. Fries and a burger before a game or boxes of processed food will only limit your energy, slow your growth, reduce your performances, and reduce your body's ability to recover. If you must eat processed foods, aim to eat the organic options. If you must grab fast-food, then stick with Chipotle or Panera Bread.

Fourth, most people think there is little difference between types of salt. For the soccer player who needs salt to stay hydrated and ensure their muscles can function properly, knowing your salts is helpful. Sea salt and table salt have similar composition, as they are both mostly sodium chloride. **Standard white table salt from salt mines is about 98% sodium chloride with the remaining 2% being anti-caking agents, chemical additives, sugar (dextrose), with no trace minerals.** They often use harsh chemicals and extreme heat when stripping away the trace minerals. Excitingly, sea salt comes from evaporated sea water. As a result, the two types of salt differ in their components, taste, and texture. According to Western Analysis, Inc., sea salt has up to 75 minerals and trace elements, making it healthier to eat than table salt.

Himalayan pink salt contains up to 84 different trace minerals. Depending on which source you read, Himalayan pink salt contains up to 15% trace minerals. **Lastly, remember that salt is still salt, just like a box of organic cookies is still a box of cookies.** Therefore, use salt sparingly. The typical American diet includes a lot of it already. Usually, I never add salt to my cooking—except for occasionally adding Himalayan pink salt to my scrambled eggs and sautéed onions on the morning of an intense workout or soccer game.

Fifth, glass containers are a better way to store and transport food. **Most foods come in plastics that contain hormone-disrupting compounds, like bisphenol-A (BPA), which have qualities that mimic the female hormone, estrogen.** Researchers at Exeter University in London studied the blood and urine of 94 teenagers aged 17-19 and found 80% had hormone-disrupting chemicals in their bodies. Bisphenol-A (BPA) can lead to conditions like cancer, thyroid disorders, and obesity. These compounds can travel into your food especially when you heat plastic containers, so never place plastic in the oven or microwave—even if the container claims to be oven/microwave safe. Therefore, stick with glass containers if you prepare meals in advance. I prefer glass containers with snap-on lids, as these keep the food fresher for longer.

Here is a quick recap of the various topics covered in this chapter for you to reference back to easily:

1. Food eating order - carb, fruit, meat, vegetable before and after activity. Vegetable, meat, fruit, carb when less active.
2. Make healthy eating easy by having healthy snacks on-hand.
3. Stay away from alcohol, smoking, drugs, processed food, and fast foods.
4. Himalayan pink salt > sea salt > table salt.
5. Avoid plastic containers.

Chapter 11

Weight Loss

Have you ever struggled with losing weight? Have you ever felt like if you dropped a few pounds, your confidence would increase? Well, this chapter is all about providing you tips and things to avoid if you are a soccer player who is interested in losing weight. Weight loss is a tough issue for most people, so this chapter reveals several things to consider so that you lose weight, and it does not return. Even if you are not interested in losing weight (and not all players need to), this chapter still has a ton of interesting information. Here are the things to watch out for when trying to lose weight:

1. Know how many calories to eat in a day.
2. Find your ideal body fat percentage.
3. Get a Fitbit.
4. Drink more water.
5. Get enough sleep.
6. Do not cut out all fat.
7. Do not go low carb on soccer days.
8. Avoid thinking there is a magic pill.

First, when starting a weight loss plan, it is important you understand what will happen when you get off the plan. Short-term weight loss will be maintained if you keep doing the things that allowed you to lose weight. **Whereas permanent weight loss requires a change in lifestyle to ensure you set up habits you can continue to do so you do not gain the weight back again.** Therefore, if there are certain weight loss things you really dislike doing, find more manageable activities which you can see yourself doing for the rest of your life. Also, competitive athletes need to lose weight differently than the average person. The average person can lose weight by fasting or cutting carbs, where as a soccer player would need to have a plan for weight loss to ensure they can perform on the field, by eating their allotted carbs around physical activity.

Weight Loss = Baseline Calories Needed + Exercise > Calories Consumed

Baseline calories are the number of calories your body would burn if you just laid in bed all day and did not move. To determine the number of calories you burned in a day, add the baseline calories to the amount of activity you did (i.e., walking, running, weightlifting, playing soccer, etc.) To lose weight, this number needs to be less than the number of calories you ate that day. **More simply, you lose weight by burning more calories than you eat.** To make it easy on yourself, go to the following website to let their calculator tell you how many calories you need to maintain your current weight and a breakdown of the macronutrients required for a person at your bodyweight.

https://www.active.com/fitness/calculators/calories

For example, at the time of writing this chapter, I am 6'0" tall and 195 lbs. I have an active lifestyle. The website indicates that it takes 3,400 calories to maintain my bodyweight. Also, it provides me a range of 383-553 grams/day of carbs, 85-298 grams/day of protein, and 76-133 grams/day of fat. Because I am always looking to add more muscle, I aim to eat at least one gram of protein for every pound I want to weigh. Therefore, I generally eat about 200 grams of protein per day. Next, I let the amount of activity I have that day determine the number of carbs I consume. On days where I am writing and working on publishing books or YouTube videos, I am less active and will consume less carbs because I do not need as much energy and I also eat more fat, so I stay full. Therefore, on inactive days, I will eat about 350g of carbs and 130g of fat.

My Inactive Days
200g protein x 4 calories/g = 800 calories from protein
300g carbs x 4 calories/g = 1,200 calories from carbs
120g fat x 9 calories/g = 1,080 calories from fat
Total = 3,080 calories (I eat less on days I am not active)

My Active Days
200g protein x 4 calories/g = 800 calories from protein.
475g carbs x 4 calories/g = 1,900 calories from carbs
100g fat x 9 calories/g = 900 calories from fat
Total = 3,600 calories (I eat more on days I am highly active)

Because 3,500 calories are roughly the number of calories in a pound, if I wanted to lose weight, I would need to eat less than the 3,400 calories needed to maintain my weight. Generally, trying to lose a pound a week (or be at a 500-calorie deficit each day) will make it manageable to achieve your goal weight without having to drop your calories and energy levels drastically. Remember that if you go back to your old habits, the weight will come back. **Almost always avoid focusing only on breaking a bad habit. Instead, replace the bad habit with a good habit.** For example, you get a sugar craving and have a bad habit of eating chocolate. A better habit would be to eat dark chocolate. A good habit when a sugar craving strikes is to eat a piece of fruit.

Second, as a soccer player with muscle, do not worry so much about your Body Mass Index (BMI) because body fat is a better way to measure your health. Doctors, dieticians, and nutritionists often judge whether a person is overweight by their BMI, but this is a scale better used for people who do not exercise. BMI treats fat and muscle the same which is not too helpful for a soccer player who has muscle mass which the average person does not. Therefore, unless you become inactive, avoid using BMI as a measure of success. A better guide is how your body looks in the mirror and what is your body fat percentage.

Using myself as an example, I have a BMI of 27, which would place me in the "overweight" category. However, I play soccer about two times per week right now and weightlift 3-4 times per week. I have visible abdominals, and a low body-fat percentage. Therefore, using myself as an example, it is easy to see that the BMI scale is faulty for someone who exercises regularly and weight trains often. Still unconvinced? Well, Cristiano Ronaldo is 6'2" and at peak condition he is 188lbs, but he is considered overweight too, which we both know is laughable!

Therefore, use the Body-Fat Rating Chart below, which applies to adults ages 18 and older, based on findings from the American College of Sports Medicine, the American Council on Exercise, and various other scientific studies. It will better help determine if you have a fit physique:

Body Fat Rating	Women	Men	Fitness Level
Risky - Low	<15%	<5%	Unsafe - See a Licensed Health Care Professional
Ultra Lean	15-18%	5-8%	Elite Athlete
Lean	19-22%	9-12%	Optimal Health and Longevity
Moderately Lean	23-30%	13-20%	Good Health
Excess Fat	31-40%	21-30%	Excessive Fat
Risk - High	>40%	>30%	Unsafe - See a Licensed Health Care Professional

Use the same website mentioned previously to determine your body fat by entering your weight, waist circumference, hips circumference, wrist circumference, and forearm circumference. Sure, there are more precise ways to measure than this method, but this will give you a great estimate of your current body fat percentage:

https://www.active.com/fitness/calculators/calories

Third, purchase a Fitbit/step counter/activity tracker. The recommended minimum of steps per day is 8,000, but a 10,000-12,000-step minimum is better if you are trying to lose weight. Walking burns the same number of calories as running, it just takes a little longer. **Getting enough steps is one of the most underrated things for weight loss.** Think about it, soccer players get a lot of steps, which helps explain why they are often one of the leanest athletes on the planet. If you are interested in more exercise tips to make sure your body is fit for game time and to give you a ton of self-confidence, then grab the *Understand Soccer* series book, *Soccer Fitness.*

Fourth, drink more water to flush out toxins from your body and improve digestion. Beverages like juice, carbonated soda pop, and alcohol have "stealth calories." These calories come in mostly undetected by our bodies. **Scientific evidence confirms that although high-calorie beverages count towards our daily calories, the body does not detect them the same way as it would recognize solid food.** By consuming solid food, people's bodies naturally compensate by reducing the remainder of their food intake. However, when people ingest liquid calories, they do not compensate for them by eating fewer calories. Richard Mattes, M.P.H, R.D., a professor of foods and nutrition at Purdue University says, *"Fluid calories do not hold strong satiety properties, do not suppress hunger and do not elicit compensatory dietary responses. When drinking fluid calories, people often end up eating more calories overall."* This explains the results of a study by researchers from Harvard University and the Children's Hospital in Boston that found women who increased their intake of sugar-sweetened beverages, gained significantly more weight than those who did not.

Fifth, obtain enough quality sleep. Too little sleep means more hours of the day awake. More waking hours generally results in more opportunities to eat food because your body is more likely to be hungry from increased waking hours. More food means more calories, which makes it difficult to lose weight. **Furthermore, not enough sleep over the long-term increases the hormone, cortisol, in your body which enlarges your appetite and increases your stress levels.** If you ever feel you have a hard time falling asleep or have a tough time staying asleep, invest in the *Understand Soccer* series book, *Soccer Sleep*.

Sixth, do not cut all fat from your meal plan. **You need fat to use the fat-soluble vitamins A, D, E, & K properly. Also, fat helps with satiation—the feeling of fullness.** In an interview with *Men's Health Magazine*, nutritionist Jaime Mass, R.D. said, *"When you remove fat from a food product, it must be replaced with other ingredients to provide a tasty and profitable alternative. So, if you take a food with fat, remove it, triple the carbs, double the sugar, add extra ingredients to support the consistency and flavor, label it fat-free and consume it for years and years, you are setting yourself up to be overweight and develop health problems, including abdominal fat, Type 2 diabetes, and cardiovascular issues."*

Even worse, processed foods like low-fat ice cream and low-fat yogurt typically contain more sugar and calories than their full-fat counterparts. Being fat-free is perfectly fine for foods like vegetables and most fruits because these are naturally fat-free. There is no processing that needs to occur to remove fat. However, avoid picking fat-free versions of food which naturally have fat in them. Personally, when I first started changing the way I ate, I cut nearly all fat from my meal plan because it made sense that fat makes you fat. However, this left me somewhat frail and very pale. Luckily, as I read and learned more, I realized the need for the macronutrient fat in a meal plan to ensure fullness and health for the person looking to lose weight.

Seventh, avoid low-carb diets like the ketogenic diet. Low carb diets are more reasonable for people who are not athletes, as they have less need for energy providing carbohydrates. As a soccer player, being in ketosis, a state where you are using fat as your primary fuel for energy, will not result in good performances on the field or training sessions. You need carbs to fuel your training and games. **If anything, reduce your carb intake on days where you do not play or have practice, but limiting carbs will make your body more lethargic on the soccer field.** The only carbs you should be interested in cutting are white bread, white rice, white potatoes, white pasta, and white sugar. These and other refined grains are low in nutrients whereas whole-grain bread, oatmeal, sweet potatoes, and brown rice are high in fiber and rich in B vitamins. Avoid an unbalanced meal plan and instead select one where you have a balance across all three macronutrients of protein, carbohydrates, and fat.

Eighth, avoid thinking there is a "magic pill" which you can take that will do the work for you. Thinking there are magic pills is not good because you develop the habit of looking for the easy way out. Thinking there are "overnight successes" is just as problematic because you do not see the 10 or so years of hard work that person did to become successful. **Leave the mindset of finding a magic pill and becoming an overnight success to other people who wish everything were easier.** The trick is knowing that things rarely get easier, you simply get better.

In conclusion, remember the following pointers to ensure you do not fall into weight loss traps which so many other people do:

1. Determine how many calories you need in a day.
2. Aim for an ideal body fat percentage.
3. Invest in an activity tracker to count your steps.
4. Avoid drinks with calories.
5. Get enough sleep.
6. Avoid fat-free foods or a fat-free diet.
7. Eat plenty of carbs on days you train or play soccer.
8. Avoid looking for magic pills and overnight success.

Chapter 12

How to Read a Nutrition Label

Nutrition Facts	
4 servings per container	
Serving size	**1 Taco (1g)**

Amount Per Serving	
Calories	**460**

	% Daily Value*
Total Fat 25g	**32%**
Saturated Fat 15g	**75%**
Trans Fat 1g	
Polyunsaturated Fat 5g	
Monounsaturated Fat 4g	
Cholesterol 200mg	**67%**
Sodium 800mg	**35%**
Total Carbohydrate 32g	**12%**
Dietary Fiber 1g	**4%**
Total Sugars 5g	
Includes 4g Added Sugars	**8%**
Sugar Alcohol 1g	
Protein 27g	**54%**
Vitamin D 0mcg	0%
Calcium 0mg	0%
Iron 5.4mg	30%
Potassium 470mg	10%
Vitamin C	35%

* The % Daily Value (DV) tells you how much a nutrient in a serving of food contributes to a daily diet. 2,000 calories a day is used for general nutrition advice.

When reading nutrition labels, the trick is to buy items that do not require nutrition labels, like bananas, avocados, apples, celery, etc. This way, you can be confident that you are getting only what you want, and not all the fillers and unhealthy ingredients which help them last months or even years on a store shelf.

However, there will be times when you will need to buy something with a nutrition label on the back. Therefore, this chapter reveals how to look at a nutrition label as an athlete. As an example, I will use a nutrition label from a popular fast-food taco chain.

Firstly, the top of the nutrition label reveals the serving size and servings per container. **Often, when you are looking at the**

nutrition label of an unhealthy food, the manufacturer will make the serving size tiny, so all the numbers on the label do not look so bad. For example, the manufacturer of a small bag of chips will say that one serving is 1/3 of the bag. But who only eats 1/3 of a small bag of chips?

Now, let us talk about calories, and calories from fat. Sadly, many people still believe that eating fat will make you fat. Fat contains nine calories per gram—unlike protein and carbohydrates, which have four calories per gram. Therefore, fat can add up quicker, but it is still vital for many fat-soluble vitamins, testosterone production, energy, and to protect your organs. **If you track your calories, this section will help you, but remember that eating higher-quality and healthier foods will go a long way towards leading a healthy lifestyle.**

Below the %Daily Value* shows the percentage of the daily values of fat, cholesterol, sodium, carbohydrates (carbs), and protein from the food. Notice the "*" asterisk at the end of %Daily Value*. **If you look farther down on the nutrition label, it explains that the "*" asterisk is showing that the above percentages are the recommendations for a person who consumes 2,000 calories per day.** Remember the charts from health.gov back in chapter one which showed the guidelines for how many calories to consume based on your age and level of activity? For a young soccer player who trains and plays several times per work, 2,000 calories are reasonable. However, for an active 16-year-old, 2,000 calories would not be enough. Not eating enough calories would leave them without enough energy in games and may result in weight loss, depending on their current size. Therefore, keep in mind how many calories you should eat to determine if the %Daily Value* applies to you or if you need to make some slight adjustments to make the numbers more relatable.

Continuing in this same section, the label lists fats, carbs, and proteins because they are the three food-related macronutrients. It also lists cholesterol and sodium because food manufacturers are required to point out these, since a large portion of Americans struggle with consuming too much sodium and have high cholesterol levels. **Sodium (e.g., table salt) makes food taste better and acts as a great preservative, so food manufacturers put large quantities of salt in their products to improve their taste and shelf life.** Some sodium (and potassium, calcium, magnesium, etc.) is necessary for the proper functioning of a hard-training soccer player's muscles. However, because there is so much salt in processed foods (e.g., pretzels, ready-to-eat meals, frozen dinners, take-out, etc.), you should not add salt to them.

An April 2017 study published in the *Journal of Clinical Investigation* confirmed that increased salt intake leads to water retention and increased appetite. Interestingly, your body tries to maintain a sodium/water ratio similar to sea water. When you consume sodium, your body holds on to water to maintain the right ratio. Consuming a single gram of table salt causes your body to retain up to an extra four cups of water, which equals roughly one pound.

Drinking more water flushes out the extra sodium, returning water levels to normal, and helps you lose water weight. You can use this knowledge to your benefit by avoiding extra salt to ensure you do not become bloated because of water weight. Also, you can consume more salt and water prior to going out in extremely hot temperature weather to ensure you have more water in your body to remain hydrated during those summer games. This will give you an advantage over your competition as they become dehydrated from the intense heat. Sadly, a high-sodium diet causes more than just water weight gain; it also increases blood pressure and increases your risk of a heart attack or stroke. Heart attack is the leading cause of death for both women and men in the United States, while strokes are the third-leading cause of death.

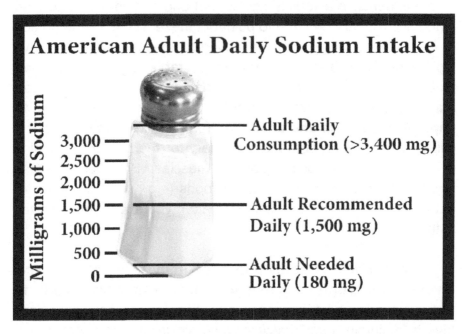

You can also notice what to expect when scanning through the ingredients at the bottom of the nutrition label. Trans-fat is a definite no-no. Many countries have banned trans-fat. There are some naturally occurring trans-fats in cheese, milk, and meats that are not too worrisome. **However, you should avoid hydrogenated oils because they increase your bad cholesterol (LDL) and decrease your good cholesterol (HDL).** If there is less than .5g of trans-fat in food, then the food manufacturer can round it down to 0g. Again, this is another reason that food manufacturers often suggest smaller serving sizes.

Also, the new guidelines set forth by the Food & Drug Administration (FDA) require food manufacturers to reveal the amount of sugar that they add to their product. Furthermore, when looking on the label under carbohydrates and you notice there is sugar alcohol, it is an easy tell that there has been processing of the food. The more processing the worse. **Sugar alcohols are** popular, low-calorie sweeteners which are partially resistant to digestion. Sugar alcohol causes bloating, diarrhea, and smelly flatulence.

The FDA recommends much less protein than a hard-training soccer player needs for muscle repair and growth. The general guideline for a hard-training athlete is based on how much you want to weigh. If you want to weigh 150 pounds, then I recommend you consume 150 grams of protein per day.

The label also lists some major micronutrients, and the number of grams of fat, cholesterol, sodium, and carbs which are recommended to eat if you consume 2,000 or 2,500 calories per day. Once you know your numbers, you can quickly look past the micronutrient and calorie section when viewing nutrition labels.

Finally, let us look at the ingredients of these tacos. The things to look for when reading an ingredient list are:
1. What is the number of ingredients?
2. Are there words you cannot pronounce?
3. Are there artificial or genetically modified ingredients?

Ingredients: Seasoned Beef: Beef, water, seasoning [cellulose, onion powder, salt, maltodextrin, soy lecithin, tomato powder, sugar, spices, citric acid, caramel color, disodium inosinate & guanylate, natural and artificial flavors, modified corn starch, lactic acid, yeast], salt, phosphates, iceberg lettuce, enriched white flour, shortening (partially hydrogenated soybean oil and hydrogenated cottonseed oil), salt, chili powder, onion, natural flavor, xylitol, sugar, baking soda, sodium acid pyrophosphate, dough conditioner (mono- and diglycerides, enzymes, wheat starch, calcium carbonate, potassium sorbate), Cheddar cheese (cultured pasteurized milk, salt, enzymes, annatto), Cheese Sauce: Nonfat milk, cheese whey, canola oil, food starch, contains 1% or less of vinegar, lactic acid, potassium citrate, potassium phosphate, sodium stearoyl lactylate, citric acid, cellulose gum, yellow 6.

First, for tacos, you should see ingredients like beef, turkey, chicken, or pork, lettuce, tomato, onion, cheese (milk, salt, enzymes), avocado, whole grain wheat, etc. These are all ingredients that you can pronounce. However, when you look at the taco ingredients on the label provided, you will see a lot more. **The large number of ingredients is a huge sign that plenty of them are bad.**

Second, the harder the ingredient is to pronounce, the higher the chance that it is not good for you. On the ingredient list, we see things like disodium inosinate, disodium guanylate, artificial flavors, partially hydrogenated soybean oil, hydrogenated cottonseed oil, xylitol, sodium acid pyrophosphate, mono- and diglycerides, potassium sorbate, potassium citrate, and sodium stearoyl lactylate. These are all hard to pronounce for most people and yep, you guessed it, they are not good for your health either.

Third, are there artificial or genetically modified ingredients in the food? Much of the health/fitness community has differing opinions on genetically modified food. There is another chapter explaining them, so I will reveal why they are not good later in this book. **However, more of the hard-to-pronounce ingredients are also artificial.** Also, there are easier-to-pronounce ingredients, like soy lecithin, maltodextrin, modified corn starch, sugar, canola oil, and vinegar which are often created from genetically modified foods like soy, canola, corn, and sugar that are sprayed with weed killers that are harmful to your health.

Additionally, when you see colors (e.g., Yellow #6) listed as ingredients, you know the product is likely not good. The U.K. and many countries have already banned food colors, but the U.S.A. is well behind the times. Researchers at Southampton University found that consuming certain synthetic dyes increased hyperactivity in kids. Also, a different U.S. study done in *Science* magazine found that children who consumed a food-dye blend performed worse on a test, as compared to another group who drank a placebo drink right before the test instead. Blue #1, Blue #2, Red #2, Red #3, Green #3, Yellow #5, Yellow #6, and Red #40 are examples of the dyes to stay away from. These can cause many types of cancer, attention disorders, chromosome damage, tumors, violent behaviors, asthma, poor sleep, allergies, and eczema.

In conclusion, knowing what to look for on a nutrition label and ingredient list will make it easier to select healthier options. Also, knowing exactly which problems, disorders, and diseases are caused by artificial and poor-quality ingredients will makes you less likely to want to eat junk food. **A pro-tip is to stay along the perimeter aisles of a grocery store and avoid going up and down the inner aisles.** The perimeter contains most of the fruits, vegetables, meats, and dairy—many of which have no nutrition labels. The inner aisles contain the highly processed foods, which all have nutrition labels because the food manufacturer must legally tell you what is in their product. Like a doctor uses X-rays to see what is going on in your body, you can use nutrition labels and ingredient lists to see what is in your food.

Chapter 13

Organic, GMO, Vegan/Vegetarian, Gluten-Free, and Paleo Diets

Has one of your friends ever started a new diet, and you wondered what they could eat? Well, this chapter discusses many mainstream diets and provides insights on the potential benefits of eating organic food.

When it comes to nutrition, you have heard a hundred times that "you are what you eat." Something you may have never heard is that **you are what your food eats,** too. Therefore, it is vital that you have high-quality food. If the cow, chicken, pig, turkey, or fish that you are eating consumed nutritious food, too, then those animals will provide more nutritional value than poorly fed animals. **This food will be much more vitamin-rich, nutrient-dense, and mineral-packed.**

Not all vegetables are created equal. Although plants do not eat other food, they do absorb nutrients from soil, and if you consume genetically modified food, then it will lack most of the rich nutrients found in organically raised fruits, vegetables, and grains. The most genetically modified foods on the market are sugar, canola, cottonseed, soy, squash, zucchini, alfalfa, and corn. These are foods for which scientists often modify to withstand harmful weed killers, which can be cancer-causing to humans. Although fewer weeds are good in theory, using harmful and synthetic weed killers to achieve it is not good. **Weed killers function as mineral chelators, which make it so that the plant sprayed with weed killer does not take as many of the nutrients from the soil.** Therefore, the same amount of protein, fat, and carbohydrates are in a genetically modified ear of corn; however, genetically modified corn has a lot less nutritional value, which is especially important for an athlete.

Organic foods are much more expensive, but they are a healthier option. If organic food is not in the budget, do not worry as there are thousands of professional soccer players who do not eat organic foods, yet can still succeed on the field. Your ability to pass, dribble, shoot, and defend are much more important for improving as a soccer player than consuming organic food over conventional options.

Organic meat, poultry, eggs, and dairy products come from animals that were not given antibiotics or growth hormones. Organic plants are grown without using most conventional pesticides, synthetic fertilizers, bioengineering, or ionizing radiation. **Organic foods do not have hidden ingredients and are not made by synthetic farming techniques. In most organic foods, what you see is what you get.**

If you are interested in some organic foods but are not willing to change everything you put in your fridge, the best places to start are:

1. Dairy
2. Fruits or vegetables that do not have a peel
3. Most frequently genetically modified foods

First, organic dairy like whole milk not only tastes richer, but it does not have added growth hormones and is less likely to upset a person's stomach given that many people have a hard time processing milk sugar, lactose.

Second, based on an analysis of test data from the U.S. Department of Agriculture, here is the full list of the dirty dozen fruits and vegetables which are great to consider eating organic:
1. Strawberries

2. Spinach
3. Kale
4. Nectarines
5. Apples
6. Grapes
7. Peaches
8. Cherries
9. Pears
10. Tomatoes
11. Celery
12. Potatoes

Third, sugar, canola, cottonseed, soy, squash, zucchini, alfalfa, and corn are the most often genetically modified foods on the market. Therefore, consider organic options instead to ensure you are consuming food which will improve your performance and not hold you back.

Next, becoming a vegetarian has become popular in recent years in the United States of America, though it dates back as early as 700 B.C. Let us discuss the different kinds of vegetarians, and the health concerns related to some types of vegetarians. **Keep in mind that this information is meant for soccer players who want to improve their nutrition for better performance and more self-confidence.**

Some of the different types of vegetarians are:

1. Vegetarian – Avoid meat, poultry, game, fish, shellfish, or by-products of animals.
2. Lacto/ovo vegetarian – Avoid all animal flesh but do consume dairy (lacto) and egg (ovo) products.
3. Vegan – Vegetarians who avoid all animal and animal-derived products as food or for other uses. This is the strictest type of vegetarian diet.

4. Pescatarian – Do not technically meet the common definition of vegetarian, but they follow a semi-vegetarian diet by eating fish and other seafood but no poultry or meat.

Why does 8% of the world's population follow a vegetarian diet? The three main reasons are for spiritual beliefs, health-concerns, and not wanting to hurt animals. **Research shows that vegetarian and vegan diets are low in saturated fat and cholesterol. Additionally, vegetarian diets contain high amounts of vitamins, minerals, fiber, and healthy plant compounds from nutrient-dense foods, like fruits, vegetables, whole grains, nuts, and seeds.** However, the vegetarian diet can be problematic for a soccer player due to its low intake of some nutrients—particularly protein, iron, calcium, zinc, vitamin D, vitamin B12, and long-chain omega-3 fatty acids.

Lacto/ovo vegetarians and pescatarians rarely have the low intakes of the previously recommended key nutrients because they are obtained easily by consuming dairy products, eggs, and fish. **Therefore, vegans must meet their protein, cholesterol, and other nutrient needs by being very planned and making sure to eat a wide variety of peas, beans, lentils, chickpeas, seeds, nuts, organic soy products, and whole grains like wheat, oats, and brown rice.** Otherwise, low testosterone, hair loss, and bruising easily are likely to occur.

So, is it helpful for a soccer player to be a vegetarian? Well, you can get by if you are a pescatarian, lacto vegetarian, ovo vegetarian, or any combination of the three. If you are a vegan, then you must plan all your meals to ensure that you can obtain the nutrients which are not readily available from plants. Also, because these types of diets often have so little protein, it is less likely that you will build muscle as quickly as your competition, and your recovery will take longer. **Therefore, you will likely be better off not being a vegetarian if improving your soccer game is your top priority.**

Like the vegetarian diet, the gluten-free diet has become very mainstream. Gluten is a substance that is present in grains, and it is responsible for the elastic texture of dough. Gluten is a general name for the proteins found in wheat, rye, oats, spelt, and barley. Not every grain contains gluten (e.g., rice and corn are gluten-free). Naturally gluten-free food groups include vegetables, fruits, meat, poultry, fish and other seafood, dairy, and nuts. **The proteins in wheat include gluten and wheat germ agglutin, which are lectins that make up the plant's natural defense system to fend off insects and humans.** These lectins are inflammatory and immuno-disruptive, which result in a negative reaction, ranging from very mild (e.g., no signs of discomfort or pain) to very severe gastrointestinal problems due to gluten intolerance (e.g., people with celiac disease that are allergic to gluten).

For the soccer player, many processed food products on grocery-store shelves contain gluten, so by not eating processed foods, you are well on your way to becoming healthier by avoiding many of the unhealthiest foods in the store. **However, unless you are allergic to gluten, do not let the minor inflammation that can occur from wheat to deter you from organic whole wheat breads or oatmeal which provide plenty of other vitamins and a lot of quality carbohydrates to fuel your performances on the field and when you work out.**

The last mainstream diet we will discuss is the Paleo diet (also known as the "Paleolithic diet", "Stone Age diet", "hunter-gatherer diet", and "caveman diet"). **It is a meal plan based on the human diets of those who lived several thousand years ago, who consumed only foods that could be gathered or hunted.** A Paleo diet typically includes lean meats, fish, fruits, vegetables, nuts, and seeds. Therefore, foods that are farmed (e.g., dairy products, legumes, and grains) cannot be consumed on this diet. This diet can be effective for a soccer player if they consume a lot of fruit to obtain the carbohydrates needed to fuel their physical activity. However, not eating dairy or farmed grains (e.g., sweet potatoes, brown rice, oatmeal, whole-grain bread, and whole-wheat pasta) will leave you with a bit less energy than your competition, and it will take longer to recover after training.

In conclusion, this chapter's purpose is to reveal the different mainstream diets and how they impact a soccer player. In all honesty, other than eating organic foods, many of the diets discussed in this chapter are not likely the best for a soccer player because they make it difficult to obtain one of the key macronutrients. Therefore, if your number one goal is great on-the-field performances, then certain diets may hold you back. In the vegetarian diet, it is difficult to get enough protein. In the Paleo and gluten-free diets, it is more difficult to obtain the carbs needed to fuel your practices and games. In a previous chapter, we discussed the fat-free diet which does not provide enough fat to help with recovery, feeling full, and effectively using the four fat-soluble vitamins.

Chapter 14

Herbs and Spices

When preparing food, it is important to balance healthy with tasty. Sure, eating barbeque sauce may be tasty, but often is not healthy. Eating food plain is healthy, but unless you are buying expensive cuts of meats and perfectly preparing your food, the food will not be too tasty. That is where herbs and spices benefit you. They merge health benefits with improved taste. Also, if you struggle with some physical pains, then use many of the herbs and spices in this chapter to reduce it. Either by taking a vitamin blend that has many herbs and spices or by incorporating it into your cooking, you will ensure that you make adding herbs and spices a habit and an easy way to boost your health and recovery. If your parents or someone else does the grocery shopping, there is a ready-to-use product mentioned at the end of this chapter that they can purchase that will help significantly.

Spice: Turmeric

What it does: Turmeric treats a variety of conditions such as arthritis, joint pain, diabetes, digestive issues, and cancer.

What foods to add it to: It is great in grain dishes (brown rice, quinoa, couscous, etc.), sauces, curries, and smoothies.

Spice: Black Pepper

What it does: Stimulates the digestive enzymes, which enhances food absorption. If you eat enough nutrients but your body cannot absorb them, then you are wasting money and some of the benefit of the food. Therefore, your body can obtain the nutrients it needs by eating more of them or being better able to use the ones it is already receiving from the foods you eat regularly. Also, black pepper has been found to have anti-tumor properties because it protects against oxidative damage by free radicals.

What foods to add it to: Use this spice in soups, salads, meat, grain dishes, eggs, potatoes, and more. One of the great things about black pepper is you can generally find it anywhere you go. Some other herbs/spices are hard to find in a restaurant or at a friend's house, but black pepper is in most places.

Spice: Cinnamon

What it does: Cinnamon improves digestion, prevents diabetes, fights infection, manages blood sugar, increases focus, and benefits cholesterol levels. Spiking and dipping blood sugar levels can drive hunger and cravings. The antioxidant compounds in cinnamon help prevent those spikes and dips by improving the way your cells metabolize blood sugar.

What foods to add it to: Use cinnamon on oatmeal, porridge, when cooking bread, toast, applesauce, apples, sweet potatoes, smoothies, cereal, cottage cheese, coffee, or plain Greek yogurt.

Spice: Garlic

What it does: Though it is not technically an herb or spice, garlic and garlic powder are great to use when cooking. Garlic reduces high cholesterol and helps with blood pressure management. Garlic destroys cancer cells and disrupts the metabolism of tumor cells, says Karen Collins, R.D., nutrition advisor to the American Institute for Cancer Research. She says, *"Studies suggest that one or two cloves weekly provide cancer-protective benefits."*

What foods to add it to: Personally, I buy a 3-pound bag of pre-peeled garlic from Costco and place it in the freezer to make it last a long time. Next, I will add to chicken, tacos, vegetable sautés, guacamole, salsas, salads, etc. Also, I will take a clove every morning, chew it, and then wash it down with water as part of supplement portion of my "morning habit mastery." If you do not have a routine for how to get a terrific start to every day, I would suggest the *Understand Soccer* series book, *Soccer Mindset*, which reveals habits to do most mornings that will give you a competitive advantage over your competition.

Spice: Ginger

What it does: With its antioxidant and anti-inflammatory properties, ginger has been used to remedy nausea, bloating, gastrointestinal discomfort, morning sickness, chemotherapy-induced nausea, weight loss, and soreness from workouts. A study found that when consuming one teaspoon of ground ginger daily for 11 days, participants experienced a 25 percent reduction in exercise-related muscle pain compared with those taking a placebo. The gingerol in ginger blocks nerve pathways which process pain.

What foods to add it to: Add ground ginger to healthy pancake, waffle, or muffin batter. Sprinkle the spice over applesauce or toast with peanut butter. You can even buy ginger root, cut off a little piece, and take it as part of your supplement routine.

Spice: Oregano

What it does: Oregano contains vitamins A, C, E, and K, as well as fiber, folate, vitamin B6, iron, calcium, magnesium, and potassium. This herb is rich in antioxidants and has anti-microbial, anti-inflammatory, and anti-cancer properties.

What foods to add to: Sprinkle oregano on fish, chicken, roasts, stews, soups, vegetables.

Spice: Cayenne Pepper

What it does: Capsaicin, the compound that gives cayenne its burn will increase your body's metabolism and help you burn more fat. Purdue University researchers found that people who added half a teaspoon of this spice to a meal ate 70 fewer calories at their next meal and craved less fatty and salty foods.

What foods to add it to: Popcorn, chicken, beef, curry, stew, chili, and Mexican food.

Spice: Paprika

What it does: Paprika is another capsaicin-containing spice derived from peppers. This ingredient has plenty of antioxidants that increase the spiciness of your food. Paprika acts as an antibacterial and stimulant which helps normalize blood pressure, improves circulation, and increases the production of saliva and stomach acids which aids digestion. Paprika also has a ton of vitamin A and contains some iron. However, avoid cooking it on high heat because it burns easily which changes its flavor and burnt foods/spices/herbs are carcinogenic (cancer-causing).

What foods to add it to: Grilled meats, eggs, soup, rice, and vegetables.

Spice: Nutmeg

What it does: Your mouth has a lot of bacteria, and nutmeg fights the germs with antibacterial compounds, which reduce plaque formation and cavity-producing microbes. Additionally, nutmeg is rich in protective anti-inflammatory compounds which can lower your risk of cancer.

What foods to add to: Add to chili, ground turkey, chicken, potatoes, carrots, pumpkin, winter squash, cabbage, broccoli, cauliflower, spinach, apples, bananas, peaches, nectarines, pears, pineapple, mango, scrambled eggs, omelets, pancakes, and French toast.

Spice: Cumin

What it does: The spice that makes Mexican food taste like Mexican food, cumin helps with weight-loss, prevents diabetes, and reduces the chances of getting cancer. Its medicinal properties come from its phenols and flavanols.

What foods to add it to: Add it to soups, stews, lentils, beans, rice, sausages, eggplant, lamb, pork, potatoes, and rice.

Spice: Rosemary

What it does: Rosemary contains vitamin A, vitamin B6, vitamin C, and other B vitamins such as folate and thiamin. It is high in fiber, has anti-inflammatory properties, and helps with digestion. Adding a bit to the meal plan is helpful for a little extra brainpower, focus, and mental clarity too.

What foods to add it to: You can brew rosemary in a tea to treat an upset stomach or nausea. Use rosemary with soups, stews, salads, chicken, lamb, pork, steaks, fish, grains, mushrooms, onions, peas, potatoes, and spinach. Rosemary oil is fantastic for skin, hair, sore spots, dryness, dandruff, and healing of cuts and bruises.

Herbs and spices add a ton of flavor, and a lot of health benefits to whatever you are cooking. Some people (me included) shy away from adding herbs and spices to food because they are afraid that they will mess up the dish. The trick is to not be afraid to experiment in your own home when no one else is eating the food. Instead of putting the herb or spice on all the food you prepared, just take one fork or spoonful of the food and add the spice to it. If it tastes good, then add it to the rest of the food, too. If it tastes bad, then try again with another fork or spoonful of the food you prepared, and a different herb or spice.

A few times experimenting in the kitchen will leave you healthier; you will recover from training easier, and you will enjoy healthier food options. **If buying all these different herbs and spices seems overwhelming, then buy blended options, like salt-free Mrs. Dash, which has over 14 flavor varieties.**

Chapter 15

Which Oils Should You Use?

With so many oils to choose from, it is difficult to know which one is best to use and if any of them will help you or hurt you as a soccer player. Some oils can help you shine, and others will leave inflammation in your body. Regardless, with all oils, a little goes a long way. Therefore, in this chapter we will discuss several oils and reveal the three you should use. These are listed roughly in order from most to least healthy.

Olive Oil

Choose an olive oil that is not overly processed. Extra-virgin olive oil has a better taste and more nutrition, as compared to refined olive oil. Extra-virgin olive oil contains unsaturated fats, which, according to multiple studies, promotes heart health. Olive oil has a low smoking/burning point, compared to other oils, so avoid cooking with it because by heating it, olive oil burns and makes it carcinogenic (cancer-causing). It is better to drizzle it on salads, pour it on rice, or use as a dip for bread.

Coconut Oil

Coconut oil is a bit of a controversial topic for many members of the health community. Due to its high saturated fat content, for a long time, people believed it was bad for your heart. Newer studies reveal that saturated animal fat differs from saturated plant fat. Coconut oil contains medium-chain triglycerides (MCTs) that are quick absorbing fatty acids that can increase the number of calories you burn. Also, these fats convert to energy easier, which makes them the ideal fat to eat before games. Also, coconut oil boosts your metabolism, curbs your appetite, and aids weight loss. One of my favorite treats is a piece of toasted bread. Let it cool for a few minutes, then spread a layer of coconut oil on the bread, followed by a layer of natural peanut butter. They combine very well and taste oddly like cinnamon rolls but without the unhealthy ingredients.

Here are some benefits of coconut oil:

1. Protects Your Skin from UV Rays
2. Increases Your Metabolism
3. Improves Your Dental Health
4. Relieves Skin Irritation and Eczema
5. Improves Brain Function
6. Moisturizes Your Skin
7. Helps Fight Infections
8. Increases Your Good HDL Cholesterol
9. Helps Reduce Belly Fat
10. Protects Your Hair from Damage
11. Decreases Hunger and Food Intake
12. Improves Wound Healing
13. Boosts Bone Health
14. Combats Candida
15. Reduces Inflammation
16. Natural Deodorant

17. Source of Quick Energy
18. Relieves Symptoms of Arthritis
19. Improves Liver Health
20. Soothes Chapped Lips

Avocado Oil

It is unrefined like extra virgin olive oil but has a much higher smoking/burning point and little flavor, making it great to cook with and use in stir-fry. Avocado oil is high in unsaturated fats and promotes healthy cholesterol levels and enhances absorption of nutrients, according to a review published in the May 2013 *Critical Reviews in Food Science and Nutrition.* Avocado oil contains vitamin E, but it is a little pricey. This heart-healthy oil has anti-inflammatory properties which help prevent arterial damage, heart disease, and blood pressure.

Ghee

Though not actually an oil, ghee is a form of clarified butter that has recently gained popularity with dairy-free eaters because the milk protein and lactose has been removed from the butter so people who are lactose-intolerant can usually eat it. It has fat-soluble vitamins with a more intense flavor than butter. Its high smoking point makes it good for cooking, but it normally is quite expensive. Therefore, grease your pan with it or use to butter bread.

Grapeseed Oil

Although often found in hair and skin products, grapeseed oil also has medicinal properties, which makes it useful as food, too. This is a great source of essential fatty acids and vitamin C. However, make sure to consume it in moderation because it also contains omega-6s, which can cause inflammation.

Sunflower Oil

This oil is high in vitamin E, has a high smoking point, and minimal flavor. Sadly, sunflower oil contains a lot of omega-6 fatty acids, which the body needs but are considered inflammatory, while omega-3s are anti-inflammatory. Sadly, many sunflower oil and sunflower seed producers use Neonicotinoids. This is an insecticide that kills our pollinating friends, the bees. Now, bees can sting you, which hurts, but getting rid of the world's best pollinator means you will not have the following foods at your grocery store, all of which need bees to grow:

Alfalfa, Almonds, Apples, Asparagus, Beans, Beets, Blackberries, Blueberries, Brussels sprouts, Buckwheat, Cabbage, Cantaloupe, Cauliflower, Celery, Cherries, Chestnuts, Chives, Clover, Cranberries, Cucumber, Currants, Eggplant, Flax, Garlic, Gooseberries, Grapes, Horseradish, Kale, Lettuce, Mustard, Onions, Parsley, Peaches, Pears, Plums, Pumpkins, Radishes, Raspberries, Rhubarb, Squash, Strawberries, Sunflowers, Sweet potatoes, Turnips, and Watermelon.

Peanut Oil

A staple of Asian cuisine, peanut oil has plenty of unsaturated fats to complement its nutty taste, nice smell, and proper use in cooking at hot temperatures. Peanut oil is high in omega-6s and impacts your omega 3:6 ratio, causing health problems. Only purchase the cold-pressed versions because the commercial peanut oils you find in grocery stores and fast-food restaurants are refined, bleached, and deodorized. Now, technically, peanuts are not a nut; they are a legume. Legumes are high in protein and fiber, but they contain some "anti-nutrients," such as phytic acid, that impair your absorption of nutrients. Therefore, eat legumes (e.g., peanut butter, peanuts, peanut oil, lentils, peas, and beans) in moderation.

Canola Oil

It is usually highly processed and derived from the genetically modified crop, rapeseed. It is used in many restaurants and fast-food chains. You are better off avoiding it.

Vegetable Oil

Vegetable oil is often a blend of canola, corn, soybean, safflower, and palm oils. You might see the word "vegetable" and think it must be good for you. Well, it is not. All vegetable oils are highly processed and have an imbalance in the recommended ratio between omega-3s and omega-6s. Vegetable oils are linked to cancer, and many other health-related issues. Also, the ingredients come from insect-repellant sprayed crops, and genetically modified organisms. To support this using the Sydney Diet-Heart study, two groups of adults consumed the same amount of oil and fat, but the first group's fat came from vegetable oil and margarine while the second group's fat came from sources like olive oil and butter. Everything else about their eating and lifestyles remained the same.

Both groups were evaluated regularly for the next seven years. The group that consumed more vegetable oil had a 62% higher rate of passing away compared to the group eating less vegetable oil.

Other Things to Watch Out for

Oils labeled as "partially hydrogenated" or "fully hydrogenated" are made from vegetable oils like soybean or cottonseed, according to the Center for Science in the Public Interest. These oils are trans fats which the Food & Drug Administration (FDA) says increase your risk for heart disease. Recently, the FDA ruled that manufacturers must remove all trans fats from their products.

In conclusion, there are many oils to use, but **the three to use as a soccer player are extra virgin olive oil, coconut oil, and avocado oil**. Use olive oil to dip bread, drizzle it on salads, or pour it on rice. Use coconut oil as an energy boosting oil before games. Use avocado oil to cook. Whatever oil(s) you end up choosing, store them away from direct sunlight to prevent oxidation. Here is a summary list of the oils in their general order of most healthy to least healthy:

Good:
1. Olive oil
2. Coconut oil
3. Avocado oil

Okay:
4. Ghee
5. Grapeseed oil
6. Sunflower oil
7. Peanut oil

Bad:
8. Canola oil
9. Vegetable oil
10. Hydrogenated oil

The following chart reveals the smoking point of different cooking oils. My recommendation is to not cook with any oils with a smoking point less than 450° to ensure that the oil does not burn and become harmful for your health. The smoking points in the image were determined by taking the average smoking points from these five sources:
1. What's Cooking America
2. Wikipedia
3. Centra Foods
4. The Spruce
5. Baseline of Health Foundation

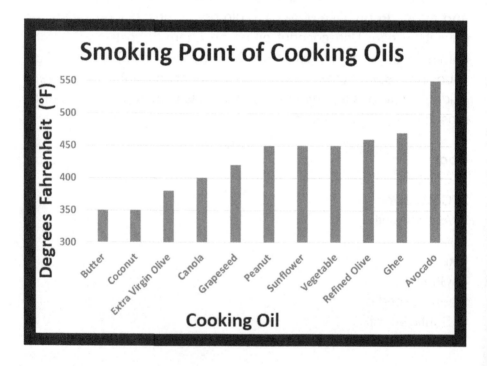

Afterword

Congrats! Because you read this book, you gained a ton of knowledge on how to take your nutrition to the next level. Implement the tips mentioned to increase your energy, improve your recovery, and make a bigger impact on your team. Understand that my first meal plan looked much different than what I currently eat today, but I started somewhere and now is the time for you to start too.

Even more importantly, you have increased your confidence. This is huge! Just by reading this book and applying the knowledge within, you have given yourself a massive advantage over your competition. You have shown that you care about eating well for your soccer career and hopefully for the rest of your life. Great job!

Excitingly, that is what a book can do. A book takes a person's decades of experiences, highs, lows, and knowledge and then condenses that information down into something which you can read in a few hours. Think about it; you just spent a few hours learning what took me a decade to figure out. Because of that, I know you will use the knowledge to improve your nutrition dramatically.

If the tips you read in this book helped your nutritional knowledge, please leave a positive review letting me know on Amazon.com.

WAIT!

Wouldn't it be nice to have an easy three-page checklist and summary guide of this book's steps? Well, here is your chance!

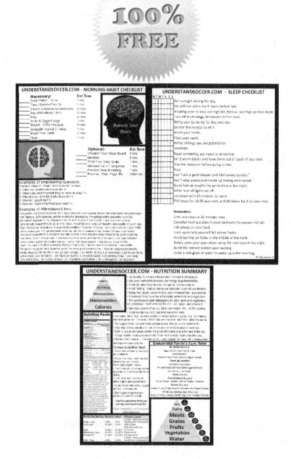

Go to this Link for an **Instant** Three-Page Printout:
UnderstandSoccer.com/free-printout

This FREE checklist and summary guide is simply a thank you for purchasing this book.

About the Author

There he was—a soccer player who had difficulties scoring. He wanted to be the best on the field but lacked the confidence and knowledge to make his goal a reality. Every day, he dreamed about improving, but the average coaching he received, combined with his lack of knowledge, only left him feeling alone and unable to attain his goal. He was a quiet player, and his performance often went unnoticed.

This all changed after his junior year on the varsity soccer team of one of the largest high schools in the state. During the team and parent banquet at the end of the season, his coach decided to say something nice about each player. When it was his turn to receive praise, the only thing that could be said was that he had scored two goals that season—even though they were against a lousy team, so they didn't really count. It was a very painful statement that after the 20+ game season, all that could be said of his efforts were two goals that didn't count. One of his greatest fears came true; he was called out in front of his family and friends.

Since that moment, he was forever changed. He got serious. With a new soccer mentor, he focused on training to obtain the necessary skills, build his confidence, and become the goal-scorer that he'd always dreamed of being. The next season, after just a few months, he found himself moved up to the starting position of center midfielder and scored his first goal of the 26-game season in only the third game.

He continued with additional training led by a proven goal-scorer to build his knowledge. Fast-forward to the present day, and, as a result of the work he put in, and his focus on the necessary skills, he figured out how to become a goal-scorer who averages about two goals and an assist per game—all because he increased his understanding of how to play soccer. With the help of a soccer mentor, he took his game from being a bench-warmer who got called out in front of everybody to becoming the most confident player on the field.

Currently, he is a soccer trainer in Michigan, working for Next Level Training. He advanced through their rigorous program as a soccer player and was hired as a trainer. This program has allowed him to guide world-class soccer players for over a decade. He trains soccer players in formats ranging from one-hour classes to weeklong camps, and he instructs classes of all sizes, from groups of 30 soccer players all the way down to working one-on-one with individuals who want to play for the United States National Team.

If you enjoyed this book, then please leave a review.

Additional Books by Dylan Joseph Available on Amazon:

Soccer Dribbling & Foot Skills: A Step-by-Step Guide on How to Dribble Past the Other Team

Soccer Defending: A Step-by-Step Guide on How to Stop the Other Team

Soccer Coaching: A Step-by-Step Guide on How to Lead Your Players, Manage Parents, and Select the Best Formation

Soccer Tryouts: A Step-by-Step Guide on How to Make the Team

Free Book!

How would you like to get a book of your choosing in the *Understand Soccer* series for free?

Join the Soccer Squad Book Team today and receive your next book (and potentially future books) for FREE.

Signing up is easy and does not cost anything.

Check out this website for more information:

UnderstandSoccer.com/soccer-squad-book-team

Thank You for Reading!

Dear Reader,

I hope you enjoyed and learned from *this book*. I truly enjoyed writing these steps and tips to ensure you feel confident in your thoughts.

As an author, I love feedback. Candidly, you are the reason that I wrote this book and plan to write more. Therefore, tell me what you liked, what you loved, and what can be improved. I'd love to hear from you. Visit UnderstandSoccer.com and scroll to the bottom of the homepage to leave me a message in the contact section or email me at:

Dylan@UnderstandSoccer.com

Finally, I need to ask a favor. **I'd love and truly appreciate a review.**

As you likely know, reviews are a key part of my process to see whether you, the reader, enjoyed my book. The reviews allow me to write more books. You have the power to help make or break my book. Please take the 2 minutes to leave a review on Amazon.com at:

https://www.amazon.com/gp/product-review/1949511316

In gratitude,

Appendix
Answer Key to Locus of Control Activity

External Locus of Control = **ELOC**

Internal Locus of Control = **ILOC**

A. It is too hard to be good at soccer these days. **(ELOC)**

B. I know it is up to me to become good at soccer. **(ILOC)**

A. Joining a good soccer team depends on me being in the right place at the right time and knowing the right people. **(ELOC)**

B. Becoming a success in soccer is a matter of hard work; luck has little or nothing to do with it. **(ILOC)**

A. What happens to me in soccer is my own doing. **(ILOC)**

B. Sometimes, I feel like I do not have enough control over the direction my soccer career is taking. **(ELOC)**

A. In the long run, people receive the respect they deserve in soccer. **(ILOC)**

B. Unfortunately, an individual's worth in soccer often passes unrecognized, no matter how hard they try. **(ELOC)**

A. The coach is the major factor in how well I play for a team. **(ELOC)**

B. I have the greatest control over how I play for a team. **(ILOC)**

A. Without the right breaks, one cannot be an effective coach of a soccer team. **(ELOC)**

B. Capable people who fail to become good coaches have not yet taken advantage of their opportunities. **(ILOC)**

A. Players who cannot get along with other players do not understand how to do so. **(ILOC)**

B. No matter how hard you try, some teammates will not like you. **(ELOC)**

A. When I make plans in soccer, I am almost always certain that I can make them work. **(ILOC)**

B. It is not always wise to plan too far ahead in soccer because many things turn out to be a matter of luck anyway. **(ELOC)**

Of the 8 statement pairings, how many external locus of control statements did you agree with? How many internal locus of control statements did you relate to? Although there are absolutely things outside your control, having a higher internal locus of control will allow you to have more confidence in your actions and an increased identity capital. It will provide you with the opportunity to ask better questions and find better answers to how you can travel from where you are to where you want to be. Believing that most of your life's circumstances are outside of your control often will lead you to not taking any action to change them. Hoping for luck is a tough thing to build a soccer career on. Instead, understand that the more you believe you can control, the more you will be able to change what you do not like and obtain more of what you enjoy.

Glossary

10,000 Hour Rule - It takes approximately 10,000 hours of deliberate practice to become an expert in a field.

80/20 Principle - 80% of your results come from only 20% of your actions.

Amino Acids - They combine to form proteins, the building blocks of life.

Antibiotics - Medicines that help stop infections caused by bacteria. They do this by killing the bacteria or by keeping them from copying themselves or reproducing.

Antioxidants - Slow or prevent damage to cells caused by free radicals, which are unstable molecules in your body.

Attacking Midfielder - A player positioned on the field between defenders and forwards and often get many assists by acting as the playmaker on the team to create scoring chances for other midfielders and forwards.

Attitude - A way of thinking or feeling about someone or something, typically one that is reflected in a person's behavior.

Bicycle Kick (i.e., "Overhead Kick") - Where you jump up and kick the ball while the ball is in the air above you.

Big 3 Foot Skills - The jab (body feint), the self-pass, and the shot fake.

Body Fat - A normal part of the human body that serves the important function of storing energy. Obesity is an excess of body fat frequently resulting in a significant impairment to health.

Body Mass Index - A weight-to-height ratio, calculated by dividing one's weight by the square of one's height and used as an indicator of obesity for non-athletes.

Caffeine - A compound that is found in tea and coffee plants that is a stimulant of the central nervous system and provides energy.

Calorie - A measure of how much energy food provides. It is the energy needed to raise the temperature of 1 gram of water through 1 °C.

Carbohydrates (Carbs) - A macronutrient broken down by the body to provide energy from sugars, starches, and cellulose.

Celiac Disease - An immune disorder in which people cannot eat gluten because it will damage their small intestine.

Challenging - Inviting competition to test one's abilities.

Champions League - The UEFA Champions League is an annual soccer competition involving the best club teams from many of the professional leagues in Europe to crown the European Club Champion. Often considered one of the top two trophies that every soccer player dreams of winning (the other being the World Cup).

Cholesterol - A waxy, fat-like substance found in all cells of the body to make hormones, vitamin D, and substances that help you digest foods.

Comfort Zone - A psychological state where things feel familiar to a person and they are at ease and in control of their environment while experiencing low levels of anxiety and stress but not growing.

Compliment - An expression of praise or admiration.

Compound Interest - The exact method of how interest is calculated in your savings account, which includes interest on principal and on other interest. With this book, it is how practicing skills can compound and be exponential.

Cortisol - The "stress hormone" that can help control blood sugar levels, regulate metabolism, help reduce inflammation, and assist with memory formulation.

Creatine Monohydrate - Similar to endogenous creatine produced in the liver, kidneys, and pancreas that helps supply energy to muscle cells for contraction.

Deliberate Practice - This form of practice is purposeful practice that knows where the player needs to go and how to get there. It is guided by an understanding of what expert performers do to excel. For example, juggling with the tops of your feet towards the toes 30 times in a row to become better at settling the ball out of the air.

Dextrose - Also referred to as glucose and is a simple sugar.

Diminishing Return Learning Curve - A learning curve where the rate of increase in skill is higher in the beginning but decreases with time until it reaches zero additional skill for more added time, at which point the person has achieved the maximum skill. This type of learning curve is most common for non-complex tasks.

DNA - The carrier of genetic information.

Driven Shot (i.e., "Sledgehammer Shot") - A shot struck with the bone of your foot, where you follow through with your entire body without crossing your legs. This is the most powerful type of shot.

Dynamic Stretches - Active movements where joints and muscles go through a full range of motion and there are no static stretches being held. These stretches are functional and mimic the movements in soccer to help your body warm up for a game.

Electrolytes - Minerals dissolved in the body's fluids, creating electrically charged ions. The most important are sodium, potassium, calcium, magnesium, and phosphate.

Empowering Questions - Open-ended questions that invite people to ponder, consider, notice, and discover things about themselves and the world around them. They create insights, "ah-ha" moments, and future opportunities.

Enzymes - Increase the rate of reactions with food in your body.

External Locus of Control - Believing external circumstances like the weather, teammates' opinions, what past coaches have taught, etc. is what shapes your future.

Failure - Giving up after a mistake without learning and applying how to correct it.

Fat/Lipids - A macronutrient to provide your body energy, support cell growth, protect your organs, keep your body warm, absorb fat-soluble nutrients, and produce important hormones.

Fat-Soluble Vitamins - Vitamins A, D, E, and K that dissolve in fats and oils. They can be stored in the body's fat stores.

Fear Zone - The zone outside of your comfort zone where you are the most vulnerable and have the lowest self-confidence because of everything that you need to learn.

Fiber - Important for regulating digestion, regular bowel movements, helps keep you feeling fuller for longer, improves your cholesterol levels, regulates blood sugar levels, and prevents diseases like diabetes and heart disease.

Fitness - Being physically fit and healthy.

Fixed Mindset - Believing your basic qualities of intelligence, talent, humor, athletic ability, etc. are fixed traits.

Fulfillment - Achieving something desired, promised, or predicted.

Futebol de Salão - Brazilian 5v5 soccer that is oftentimes played on a basketball court.

Future Truth - Statements that are not currently true but will become true in the future through belief and action in the present.

Gastrointestinal - Related to the stomach and intestines.

Genetically Modified Organisms (GMO) - Organisms whose genetic material has been artificially manipulated in a laboratory through genetic engineering, which creates plants, animals, bacteria, and viruses that do not occur in nature or through traditional crossbreeding methods.

Gifted - Having exceptional talent or natural ability.

Gluten - A protein substance present in many grains and responsible for the elastic texture of dough. Gluten functions as a plant's natural defense system to fend off insects and humans from eating them.

Glycogen - Excess blood sugar stored in the body.

Gratitude Journaling - Writing at least three things you are grateful for each day.

Growth Hormone - A hormone that stimulates growth in animal cells including muscles.

Growth Mindset - Believing your basic qualities of intelligence, talent, humor, athletic ability, etc. are abilities you have developed over time using knowledge and hard work.

Growth Zone - Where your dreams in soccer become a reality. This zone allows you to be okay with making mistakes because you know that you will contribute to your team's success every single game. You experience some anxiety in this zone but can turn it into motivation and fuel for productivity.

Habitual/Regular Practice - The most common form of practice where a person goes through the motions, repeating what they normally do, without being challenged or having a set goal. For example, practicing shooting from the penalty spot for the fifth practice in a row.

Himalayan Pink Salt - Salt containing up to 84 different trace minerals. It can be made of up to 15% trace minerals.

Hormones - A regulatory substance produced in humans and transported in tissue fluids such as blood or sap to stimulate specific cells or tissues into action.

I Am - Most statements you attach to the words "I am" often become true in your life.

Identity Capital - Belief in who you are as a person and your ability to decide things for yourself.

Identity Crisis - A period of uncertainty and confusion in which a person's sense of identity becomes insecure, typically due to a change in their expected aims or role on a soccer team or in life.

Increasing Return Learning Curve - A learning curve where the more time spent learning makes it easier to learn more things. For example, a soccer player is acquiring skills, speed, and strength at an ever-increasing rate during their competitive career. This type of learning curve is most common for complex tasks.

Inflammation - The immune system's response to injury and infection to tell the immune system to heal and repair damaged tissue, as well as defend itself against foreign invaders, such as viruses and bacteria.

Insoluble Fiber - Does not dissolve in water or in your body and remains unchanged as it moves through you before being pooped out. It acts as a cleaner that travels through your body scrubbing the walls.

Insulin - Regulates the amount of glucose in the blood.

Internal Locus of Control - Believing your own work ethic, perseverance, mindset, attitude, and feelings are ultimately what determine your future.

Ketogenic - A low-carb diet emphasizing protein and fat and minimizing carbohydrates.

Lacto Vegetarian - Someone who does not eat meat or eggs, but who eats dairy products.

Lactose - Milk sugar made up of glucose and galactose.

Learning Curve - Describes how much time is needed to master something.

Learning Zone - The zone after the fear zone where you will pick up the skills and abilities needed to overcome your problems and challenges. This zone requires work but is the last step before achieving your goal in the growth zone.

Locus of Control - How much a person believes they can control the outcomes of events in their lives.

Loss Prevention - Taking measures to prevent losing which often detracts from focusing on winning.

Macronutrition - Fats, proteins, and carbohydrate required in large amounts in the diet.

Meal Timing - Planning meals and snacks for specific times throughout the day to manage hunger, improve performance, and help recovery.

Meditation - Thinking deeply or focusing your mind for a period of time, in silence for spiritual purposes or as a method of relaxation.

Mentor - An experienced and trusted adviser who can take their experiences and direct you on how to achieve your goals and dreams much more quickly.

Micronutrition - Vitamins and minerals needed in smaller amounts than macronutrients.

Mindset - The established set of attitudes and beliefs held by someone.

Minerals - Help with growth, bone health, fluid balance, and several other processes.

Mistake - A wrong action.

Moving First Touch (i.e., "Attacking Touch") - Pushing the ball into space with your first touch, which is the opposite of taking a touch where the ball stops underneath you (i.e., at your feet).

Never Miss A Cone - The idea that skills compound so missing cones in practice limits the number of opportunities you have to get better.

Nutrition - Food necessary for health and growth.

Nutrition Label - The nutrition information panel required on most packaged food in many countries showing what nutrients are in the food.

Opposite Foot - Your non-dominant foot. Out of your two feet, it is the one you are not as comfortable using.

Organic - Generally, foods without the hidden ingredients and farming techniques that the government does not require manufacturers put on food labels. What you see is what you get in most instances.

Ovo Vegetarian - Someone who does not eat meat or dairy, but who eats eggs.

Paleo Diet - A meal plan based on human diets of those who lived several thousand years ago by consuming only foods that could be gathered or hunted like lean meats, fish, fruits, vegetables, nuts, and seeds.

Panic Zone - Burning out and distance yourself from learning new skills because you try to take on too much at once. In this zone, you will find yourself not being as excited about soccer as you are when you learn just one thing in-depth at a time.

Parenting - Raising a child.

Pescatarian - Someone who chooses to eat a vegetarian diet, but who also eats fish and other seafood. Often, they also eat dairy and eggs too.

Phytonutrients - Give fruit and vegetables their colors and help protect against diseases.

Preservative - Added to food to prevents the growth of microorganisms as well as slowing the oxidation of fats that cause food to expire.

Process Behaviors - What a soccer player has control over and can perform regardless of how the game is unfolding. Things like being aggressive, playing hard, staying level-headed, keeping your head up, having fun, communicating, and being positive with yourself and teammates.

Protein - A macronutrient made up of many amino acids that help aid in normal cell function, muscle growth, creating enzymes, producing hormones, and can be used for energy too.

Psychology - The scientific study of the human mind and its functions, especially those affecting behavior in a given circumstance.

Purposeful Practice - Practice where you set specific goals for what you want to complete successfully. For example, I want to juggle the ball 30 times without letting it hit the ground.

Reframing - A way of viewing and experiencing events, ideas, concepts, and emotions to find more positive alternatives.

S.M.A.R.T Goal - Setting a goal that is specific, measurable, attainable, relevant, and timely.

Sandwich Feedback Technique - Giving a compliment, then providing constructive feedback, and finishing with another compliment to ensure someone hears your words but does not resent your feedback.

Saturated Fat - Solid at room temperature and found in meats, coconut, and palm kernel oil.

Scissor - When the foot closest to the ball goes around the ball as you are attempting to dribble an opposing player. Emphasize turning your hips to fake the defender by planting past the ball with your foot that is not going around the ball, so you can use the momentum of the moving ball to your advantage.

Self-Image - The idea one has of one's abilities, appearance, and personality.

Shot Fake - Faking a shot. Make sure your form looks the same as when you shoot, including: 1) Looking at the goal before you do a shot fake 2) Arms out 3) Raise your shooting leg high enough behind your body, so it looks like you are going to shoot.

Silver Lining - Finding a positive aspect in something negative.

Simple Interest - The quick and rough method of calculating interest in your savings account, which only has the interest on the principal. With this book, it is how players view practicing skills as additive even though building abilities is exponential (as shown through compound interest).

Smoking Point - The burning point/temperature at which an oil begins to degrade and become harmful for your health.

Sodium - A mineral found in salt that is abundant in nature and is used to flavor and preserve food.

Soluble Fiber - Dissolves in water and in gastrointestinal fluids when it enters your body's stomach and intestines. It changes into a gel-like substance that bacteria in your body digests.

Subconscious Mind - An unquestioning servant that works day and night to make sure your behavior fits a pattern consistent with your emotionalized thoughts, hopes, beliefs and desires.

Sugar Alcohol - Low-calorie sweeteners that are partially resistant to digestion and cause bloating, diarrhea, and smelly flatulence.

Supplement - A product taken by mouth that contains a dietary ingredient like vitamins, minerals, amino acids, herbs, and other substances.

Synovial Fluids - A fluid found in the cavities of joints that reduces friction between the cartilage of the joints during movement.

Talent - Naturally have the skill, gifts, and aptitude.

Testosterone - A hormone that is the most potent of the naturally occurring androgens that cause strengthening of muscle tone and bone mass.

Threatening - Causing someone to feel vulnerable or at risk.

Toxins - Natural substances covering a large variety of molecules, generated by fungi, algae, plants, or bacteria metabolism. These have harmful effects on humans—even at very low doses.

Trace Minerals - You only need a small amount of these minerals, which include iron, manganese, copper, iodine, zinc, cobalt, fluoride, and selenium.

Trans Fat - Chemically created in a factory by hydrogenating oils and it is bad for your heart health.

Unsaturated Fat - Liquid at room temperature and considered beneficial fats because they can improve blood cholesterol levels, ease inflammation, stabilize heart rhythms, and play several other beneficial roles.

Vegan - A person who does not eat or use animal products including seafood, eggs, and dairy.

Vegetarian - Someone who avoids meat, poultry, game, fish, shellfish, or by-products of animals.

Vision Board - A tool used to help clarify, concentrate, and focus on life goals. It is any board on which you display images that represent whatever you want to be, do, or have in your life.

Visualization - Mentally rehearsing the game situations you are likely to come across to ensure you know how you will react.

Vitamins - Necessary for energy production, immune function, blood clotting, and other functions.

Water-Soluble Vitamins - Vitamins B and C are not stored in the body, so they must be taken in daily.

Winger - Playing in the flanks, these attackers' opposition are usually the other team's full backs. Their role is like that of outside midfielders, except these attackers play farther up the field and are expected to score significantly more than outside midfielders.

Acknowledgments

I would like to thank you, the reader. I am grateful to provide you value and to help you on your journey of becoming a more confident, tougher, well-rested, and healthier soccer player. I am happy to serve you and thank you for the opportunity to do so. Also, I would like to recognize people that have made a difference and have paved the way for me to share this book with you:

I want to thank the grammar editor Abbey Decker. Her terrific understanding of the complexities of the English language ensured that the wording needed to convey the messages was appropriate and she provided countless grammatical improvements.

Also, I would like to thank the content editors Kevin Solorio, Michael Mroczka, Toni Sinistaj, and Youssef Hodroj. They reviewed this book for areas that could be improved and additional insights to share that could immediately help you, the reader.

Many thanks,

Dylan Joseph

Made in the USA
Las Vegas, NV
03 April 2024

88184236R00174